MINING
IN THE
YORKSHIRE
DALES

BY JOHN MORRISON

Dalesman Publishing Company
Stable Courtyard, Broughton Hall,
Skipton, North Yorkshire BD23 3AE

First Edition 1998

Text and colour photographs: © John Morrison 1998
Maps: Jeremy Ashcroft
Cover photograph: The remains of Old Gang Lead Smelt
Mill by John Morrison

A British Library Cataloguing in Publication record is available
for this book

ISBN 185568 138 2

Printed by Midas Printing (HK) Ltd

LEAD MINING
IN THE
YORKSHIRE DALES

BY JOHN MORRISON

Contents

Thanks to

Lawrence Barker
Mike Gill
Frank Burns
Peter Hodge
Robert White
But any mistakes are mine ...

Section One

Introduction

Visitors flock to the Yorkshire Dales to enjoy the fells, valleys and the "quiet recreation" enshrined in the philosophy of the National Parks. At first sight it all seems so tranquil, so rural: a reassuringly long way from the noise and bustle of our industrial cities. But the Industrial Revolution did not pass the Dales by, as can be seen by the number of mines and quarries, and the old mills whose remains can still be found alongside many rivers and becks.

Far from being some pastoral idyll, the northern Dales have long been exploited for their mineral riches. Lead has been the most important, and the one that transformed the landscape most dramatically. If we could travel 150 years back in time we would discover a major industry supporting a much larger population than is to be found in the area today. The population of Swaledale and Arkengarthdale, for example, was three times what it is now; the difference is largely due to the expansion – and the subsequent extinction – of the lead mining industry. Mining underpinned the economy of these two isolated valleys; farming, by comparison, was almost a sideline.

Many of the mine workings are now dilapidated and 'going back to nature', but if you walk up the steep-sided valley of Gunnerside Gill, or raise your eyes to the skyline of Arkengarthdale, you will begin to understand both the scale and the importance of lead mining.

Whole communities in the Dales were reliant on lead mining, and villages grew up to accommodate the influx of miners and their families. There was a living to be made for those prepared for hard, dangerous work ... but precious few fortunes. At best a miner could look forward to buying or renting a smallholding, on which to keep a cow, and to be able to supply the basic needs of his family. His

5

Lead Mining in the Yorkshire Dales

lifespan might be an average of ten years shorter than that enjoyed by those in other trades; forty-five to fifty years of age was typical.

When the industry died, late last century, the miners had to look elsewhere for work. Some of them moved further north, to the Durham coalfields. Some moved to the burgeoning industrial towns of Lancashire and Yorkshire to work in the textile mills. There was work to be had, and regular wages, though the conditions they had to endure would sometimes have been no better than they had known in the Dales.

Other miners decided their futures lay overseas and, on the basis of encouraging reports coming back from early settlers, decided to try their luck in the mines of the United States.

This exodus quickly depopulated many of the Yorkshire Dales. Even with the more recent influx of second home owners, these numbers have never been made up. Today, lead mining in the Dales provides merely a footnote in the annals of industrial history.

It is unlikely that anyone could again mine for lead in the Yorkshire Dales. The National Park has upheld, for the past forty years, a remit to "maintain the Dales for quiet enjoyment", and mining would definitely run contrary to that philosophy of conservation. Yet five smelt mills (Grassington, Grinton, Marrick, Old Gang and Surrender) have been designated as Scheduled Ancient Monuments. The fabric of these fascinating and historic buildings is being consolidated, as tangible reminders of a once vital industry.

Those visitors to the Dales who leave their cars behind, and take to the hills, will notice arched tunnels that lead, intriguingly, straight into the hillsides. They will see clusters of buildings that were obviously designed for some industrial process. They will see flues, chimneys and extensive spoil heaps that even today are bare and unsupportive of plant life. These remains are those of lead mines and the mills in which the crude lead ore was smelted into ingots.

There are a number of books on lead mining available, but they tend to fall into one of two categories. Firstly, there are a number of weighty, scholarly tomes, written by specialists in mining history. Though fascinating to the mining enthusiast, they are unlikely to

Introduction

engage the attention of more general readers. Secondly, there are one or two slim volumes whose attempts to cover the subject seem all too brief.

I feel there might be room for a book that takes the middle way: telling the story of the mines and miners, without getting bogged down in statistics and technicalities (and not a footnote in sight). In addition I wanted to direct readers towards some of the more interesting lead mining sites in the Yorkshire Dales, and to interpret what they will see there. I wanted to answer the most obvious questions about the industry, but avoid less engaging topics such as the convoluted histories of individual mining concerns or the legal wrangles that kept so many of them at loggerheads.

I met a woman, on one of my rambles around the mines, who said, rather wistfully: "You know, I wish the mines were still working today." Well, I think I know what she meant. I took it that she wasn't yearning for a time when she might have laboured down the mines. Nor, presumably, did she yearn to have been married to a lead miner, enduring the many privations of such a harsh and insecure existence. No, I assume she wanted to go back in time, with her late 20th century sensibilities intact, to see what these lonely mining sites were like when thousands of men, women and children were labouring there.

Many of those who have explored these sites must feel the same. Wouldn't it be fascinating to go back in time to, say, 1850, and be able to spend one single day at a working mine? Yet I have tried not to romanticise the life of the miners: they seldom had security of employment or a guaranteed income during those periods when they were employed.

There used to be a tradition – brought to a fine art in guidebooks of Victorian days – of seeing the country in terms of picturesque tableaux, peopled with locals who had little purpose other than to add a sense of scale to the landscape painters' compositions. And few writers wrote prose more purple than Halliwell Sutcliffe, in his book *The Striding Dales*.

He described the lead miners of Greenhow Hill, and their

superstitions. They "knew the mystery things that happen in the underworld, where galleries probe into the tortured bowels of the earth, and the spirits prisoned there resent intrusion. They were not fanciful men, the Greenhow miners, but quiet, stalwart, prone to say little. It was hard to break their reticence; yet once in a long while they would speak of hidden matters. There was one who reached the mine head before his fellows, and went down the ladders alone, impatient for his work. They came later on and found him dead in a narrow gallery, with queer marks about his throat. Well, poor lad, he should have known it was not good to go singly into any mine. The trolls fear numbers, but are wolves on the track of a lonely man. That was his comrades' summing up."

There were many fears and fancies associated with the mines: superstitions, phantom footsteps, supernatural warnings of imminent danger. It was considered unlucky to whistle underground, for example, or to allow a woman down a mine.

Most writers commended the lead miners on their sober habits, willingness to work hard, and their desire to better themselves through attending both chapel and institute. Most writers, but not all. Arthur Young, writing in 1770, found less to admire: "Miners in general ... are a most tumultuous, sturdy people, greatly impatient of control, very insolent, and much void of common industry ... No bribes can tempt them to any other industry after the first performance of their work, which leaves them half a day for idleness, or rioting in the alehouse ..."

Daniel Defoe, author of *Robinson Crusoe,* also wrote *A Tour Through the Whole Islands of Great Britain*, published in 1724. Of a lead miner he wrote: "For his person, he was lean as a skeleton, pale as a dead corpse, his hair and beard a deep black, his flesh lank, and, as we thought, something of the colour of lead itself, and being very tall and very lean he looked ... like an inhabitant of the dark regions below, and who was just ascending into the world of light."

The dangers themselves were real enough. Though there were few problems with the toxic gases that plagued the coal miners, there was the everyday reality, throughout a shift, of breathing in rock dust. The

Introduction

Dr A Raistrick

The lead miners of Greenhow Hill were, it seems, just as superstitious as those anywhere else in the Dales. This is Cockhill Smelt Mill, Greenhow, Nidderdale, circa 1910.

dust levels increased with every explosive charge laid; miners could not afford to let the air clear before venturing back to the mine head with their picks and shovels. Even without the dust the air was commonly foul, with the levels so poorly ventilated that the miners' candles sputtered out.

The mines themselves may be off limits today to all save experienced cavers, and mining buildings may be in poor state of repair, but evocative names live on. Who could be unmoved by the optimism of naming a mine the Wonderful Level? Or the Prosperous Smelt Mill? And what unfulfilled expectations are revealed by the Hard Level, the Hungry Hushes or the Folly Vein? The origins of other names are lost, and we can only guess at the incidents that caused the Brandy Bottle Incline, the Blue Joke Vein and the Spirit Level to be so called.

Lead Mining in the Yorkshire Dales

The idea for this book crystallised one day when I was exploring the stunning lead mining scenery of Gunnerside Gill in Swaledale. I had stopped for a breather, and to take in the spectacular view which – as far as the eye could see – had been created by mining. Huge hushes had riven both sides of the valley. Spoil heaps and mining debris scarred the hillsides; screes of mined rock shelved down to Gunnerside Beck. As I sat, a group of hikers approached and stopped close enough for me to overhear snatches of conversation. As they stared out over this scene of mining devastation, one of them remarked: "You know, I've heard that there were mines up here, but I really don't know where ..." Like the film characters who couldn't see a dinosaur's footprint simply because they were standing in it, this group couldn't spot the mines simply because everything in view belonged to the long-gone era of lead mining!

Warning

The six walks in this book guide you around some of the most interesting mining fields in the Yorkshire Dales. They are all above ground.

The fabric of the mines has seen little maintenance for a century or more, leaving many levels and shafts in a very dangerous condition. Unlike the caves and pot holes in the limestone areas of the Yorkshire Dales, mining levels are intrinsically unstable. For example, unproductive mining waste was often piled onto wooden platforms in mined-out areas underground, to save the trouble of bringing it out of the mine. These wooden structures, now rotten, present unforeseen perils to those who explore the mines today. Shafts, too, were often sealed off with wood. They can now give way underfoot, with potentially fatal results.

My advice is to stay well clear of all underground workings. If you wish to explore them, join one of the groups (see Societies section) that exists to learn more about the mines and the men who worked in them.

History

L ead has a long history. As far back as 2,500 BC this most
malleable of metals was being used in Egypt and Mesopotamia
to make vessels and ornaments.

Lead mining in Britain dates back at least two thousand years.
Lead ornaments and jewellery have been excavated from pre-Roman
burial grounds, and the Romans exploited the rich Pennine veins for
lead that they used for roofing, plumbing and paint pigments.

It is thought that they enslaved those native Brigantians who dared
offer resistance to Roman rule, and set them to work in penal
colonies. The lead mines at Hurst, in Swaledale, were probably
worked in this way, and lead from this wild and windswept outpost
may have graced the roof of no less a building than St Peter's in
Rome.

A small number of Roman lead ingots have been found, near Hurst
and Greenhow Hill; they bear the names of Roman emperors
(including Trajan and Hadrian) which enable them to be dated with
some accuracy.

The Roman occupation of Britain finally came to an end in 410
AD. Successive waves of Anglo Saxons and Scandinavians first
invaded and then settled. The fact that so many of these settlers chose
inhospitable upland areas to live – rather than the more easily farmed
lowlands – indicates that the presence of lead might well have been a
significant factor.

Few extant records relate to mining during medieval times, though
it is likely that many settlements in the Yorkshire Dales grew in size
and importance due to mining rather than agriculture. After the
Norman Invasion of 1066, lands in the northern counties were
granted to many of those who had given proof of their allegiance to
King William. Lead mines formed an important part of these
transactions, and the mineral rights typically passed into the control
of lords of the manor.

Aristocratic landowners shared the spoils with the monks of the

Lead Mining in the Yorkshire Dales

great Yorkshire abbeys, who seem to have had few scruples about trying to serve both God and Mammon. For two centuries, until King Henry VIII took away their power and razed their buildings, much of Swaledale was in the control of Bridlington Priory and Rievaulx Abbey.

The monks of these and other abbeys – such as Bolton, Fountains and Jervaulx – had great influence during this period. They farmed extensive lands (known as granges) throughout the Yorkshire Dales. The monks kept cattle, and possibly began a tradition of cheese-making that continues today – most notably in Wensleydale.

After the dissolution of the monasteries the King granted the Swaledale manors to noblemen who had given him loyal service – among them Thomas Wharton, whose descendants were to play major roles in the mining of lead in the dale. It was, ironically, the stripping of lead from the roofs of Yorkshire's great religious houses that produced a glut in the lead market for the next few years. Lead totalling 500 tons was removed from Rievaulx Abbey alone.

John Leland, writing about 1540, observed that "The men of Sualdale (ie Swaledale) be much usid in digging Leade Owre from the great hills on each side of Sualdale."

Of course, those who held the mineral rights were not necessarily those who ventured underground, and it is likely that miners worked the veins under some sort of agreement (similar to the system of tithing) that saw a certain proportion of mined ore being paid to the mine owners.

Until the 1670s miners had customary rights to exploit the mines. Later, the rights were sold (or let) to larger mining concerns, who were able to raise sufficient capital to work the mines more efficiently. The miners were consequently banished to less productive areas, or were forced to work for one of the larger partnerships.

Mining techniques were probably more primitive at this time than they had been during the Roman occupation. The Germans, however, had developed a more scientific approach, and much of their knowledge was enshrined in a book, called *De Re Metallica*, published in 1556. During the reign of Elizabeth I, German miners were encouraged to settle in Britain, and impart some of their mining expertise to their British counterparts.

The industry increased in importance as great houses were being built – and rebuilt – during the sixteenth century. Lead became particularly valuable as a malleable and weatherproof roofing material.

Landowners were, by the 1670s, taking a more active role in lead mining activities. Instead of just taking royalties from mining partnerships, they were often able to supply the venture capital the miners lacked. This allowed more ambitious – and therefore more costly – projects to be undertaken, such as exploiting the deeper veins or creating much-needed drainage levels.

The industry thrived, and by the eighteenth and nineteenth centuries Britain was the biggest producer of lead in the world. It is from these two centuries that most surviving smelt mills and subsidiary buildings can be dated.

The rights to negotiate 'bargains' with the landowners were granted, during the 19th century, to those who had first discovered the existence of lead. This gave miners the incentive to spend time prospecting. Landowners were, naturally enough, as keen as the miners to profit from mineral finds on their land.

Lead mining never became a highly mechanised industry in the Pennines; the sheer isolation of most sites saw to that. While the Industrial Revolution was transforming for ever the patterns of work for millions of city dwellers, the lives of the lead miners were little changed. The biggest advance was the harnessing of water, via huge wheels, to power some of the mining and dressing processes that had previously been done by hand. Rock drills, powered by compressed air, began to be used towards the end of the 19th century, but by this time the industry was in irreversible decline. Most lead miners still attacked the mine face with the age-old tools of their trade: pick and shovel, plug and feather.

Right up to the end of the last century, lead mining relied heavily on men (and women and children) doing dirty and laborious jobs. By the time the technology was available to exploit lead more efficiently, the demand was being met from other, cheaper sources in Europe and elsewhere.

Lead ore usually occurs in vertical veins; when these veins were found close to the surface they were generally exploited by open cast mining. That is, access to the veins was from ground level, with all mining activities open to daylight. Naturally, there was a limit to the depth that could be achieved by this method.

A more efficient way of exploiting a vein was to dig a vertical shaft on the course of the vein. When the shaft was deep enough – or when the water table prevented digging any further – miners would tunnel sideways along the vein. The extent of horizontal exploration in any one shaft was limited by the danger of collapse, and the amount of ventilation. To ensure a degree of safety, lengths of timber were used to shore up unstable workings. If collapse seemed imminent the workings were simply abandoned.

When digging these primitive shafts – commonly known as bell pits – the main problem was getting waste material up to ground level, and disposing of it. Once the hole was too deep for the digger to deposit each shovelful of earth around the perimeter of the shaft, other tactics had to be employed. The simplest method of bringing the waste to the surface was by using a jack roller or windlass: a hand-operated winch that raised a laden bucket, known as a kibble. Surplus water could be brought out the same way.

These bell pits were unconnected, except for the fact that they tended to be dug in straight lines, along the known extent of a vein. As one bell pit was abandoned, another would be dug perhaps thirty metres away. This process continued until the vein ran out, or became too deep to reach.

Hundreds of collapsed bell pits can be seen in the Yorkshire Dales, particularly in Swaledale and Arkengarthdale. They are not hard to find, though they can often be confused with coal pits and natural sink holes. Look for circular depressions in the ground, commonly ten feet or so in diameter. Natural collapsing – and later infilling – may have left only a saucer-shaped hollow. Typically, bell pits are surrounded by circular spoil heaps. The other feature that

Dr A Raistrick

Shafts were mostly used in the extensive mining field on Grassington Moor in Wharfedale. This is the Condenser House on the flue from Cupola Smelt Mill, Grassington Moor.

distinguishes these old mining shafts from natural depressions is that they are usually to be found in straight lines – sometimes extending hundreds of metres across the fells.

To stop people and sheep from falling into old, abandoned bell pits, many were covered over with wood and then turfed. Once the wood has rotted, however, the dangers are merely increased by being disguised.

Hushing is a mining technique that may have been practised from the earliest days of lead mining, and it continued right up to the industry's decline a century ago. It used the abrasive action of fast-running water to remove loose rock and topsoil – giving miners access to the lead-bearing veins beneath – and could only be used in steeply sloping sites.

Dams were built on the crest of a hill directly above the area to be hushed. Rainwater was collected, and streams diverted, to produce temporary lakes. When the water level was high enough, men broke the dams and allowed the torrent of water to rush downhill, tearing at the soil and rubble in the process. Miners hoped that new areas of lead-bearing vein would be exposed. Even the piles of rubble left at the bottom of the hill would be picked over for the presence of ore-bearing minerals.

Productive sites would be subjected to repeated hushing, creating rocky gullies of such a size that most observers would imagine they were natural rather than man-made. A substantial stretch of Gunnerside Gill, for example, is made up of three massive hushes – Bunton, Friarfold and Gorton – that create an almost lunar landscape on which, even now, a century on, vegetation refuses to grow.

Hushing was an appropriate way of reaching accessible veins in hilly terrain, whereas bell pits were generally dug on flatter ground. Bell pits enabled miners to reach a vein from above, but allowed only limited exploration along its length. Poor ventilation, waterlogged workings and the possibilities of a cave-in were ever-present problems, too. Miners were aware that richer pickings could be found by following the veins further into the hillsides than could be managed by shallow, unconnected bell pits. So the next step was to extend the horizontal tunnels deeper into the hillsides.

Lead mining sites in the Yorkshire Dales are typically riven by steep-sided valleys and gullies. The veins could be reached in two ways: by tunnelling into the hillsides, or, from above, by digging shafts down from the moor tops. We can find both vertical shafts and horizontal tunnels (known as levels or adits) in most of the mining sites in the Dales. Flatter areas, such as the extensive mining fields of Grassington Moor, had no convenient valley from which to drive levels, so shafts were mostly used.

Vertical shafts were dug by hand, often lined with stones and reinforced with wooden stemples, to maintain the full width of the shaft even when driven through soft, friable soil. Shafts provided a convenient route for bringing ore, water and mined waste (known as deads) to the surface.

History

Many shafts were topped by some form of winding gear, whether driven by hand or a horse whim. The depth from which material could be lifted was largely dependent on the weight of rope and number of horses being used. Hauling ore from great depths remained impracticable until mechanical systems were introduced, powered by water or steam. Some shafts – usually narrower – were dug specifically to give miners access, with wooden rungs set at regular intervals into the sides of the shaft.

These shafts can still be found today, though many of them have been blocked up to stop sheep – or foolhardy walkers – falling into them. It's hard to stare down into the Stygian depths of an open mining shaft without feeling a shudder of apprehension. It's harder still to imagine climbing down into the blackness, day after day, for a six-hour shift.

Where the terrain was suitable (with veins crossed by steep-sided valleys), near-horizontal tunnels were driven deep into the hillsides. Entrances to these levels can be spotted in many mining sites in the Dales. The tunnel entrance is typically a neat arch of dressed stone, leading into a long tunnel. This arched profile was repeated whenever progress was through unstable ground and the roof needed reinforcing. The presence of these arched entrances is a sure sign of former mining activity, even when other evidence is scant.

Adits were often driven into a hillside at the base of a hush. Since ore-bearing veins typically occur in the vertical plane, the chances were good that a level could be dug to connect with the same vein lower down. It was important to maximise the chances of meeting a profitable vein, as tunnel-building was slow, costly and labour intensive. Unfinished adits bear mute witness to aborted plans and shattered dreams.

Water was a constant problem for the miners. Beneath the water table, mines were liable to flood, and heavy rains could swamp mine workings at any depth. At best, the miners worked in uncomfortably damp conditions; at worst the adits could become subterranean rivers. So it was that most adits were driven into the hillside at a slight upward incline to help drain water from the mine workings.

Lead Mining in the Yorkshire Dales

An incline also facilitated the removal of mined material. It was easier to pull an empty waggon uphill into the mine-workings than a laden one. Look carefully at a tunnel entrance, and you may see the remains of a narrow trackway made of iron rails. Along these simple railways the waggon wheels ran. The waggons were usually manhandled in and out, though some adits were made sufficiently wide and tall for ponies to do the hauling.

As mining techniques grew more sophisticated during the early years of the 19th century, and mining companies began to bring much-needed venture capital into the industry, mines became ever more complex systems of interconnected shafts and adits. While self-employed miners could not afford to drive levels through unproductive ground, well-financed mining companies could take a longer-term view of their enterprises. It might take a year or longer to make any profit at all from a speculative level, and then only after bearing the considerable costs of tunnelling.

So it was that cross-cut levels were driven, to exploit new areas of vein, or simply to drain excess water. The expense could be justified by the promise of potential future gain. Nevertheless, lead mining was always a high-risk business. Tales of rich, productive veins are outnumbered by sad chronicles of unfulfilled ambitions, and abandoned workings.

A typical Pennine mine of the mid-19th century was a complex system of shafts, levels and cross-cuts. You could enter a mining level in Swaledale and make your way (assuming you *knew* your way ...) through a tracery of levels, rises and sumps which would eventually bring you out into the daylight of Arkengarthdale, six miles away from where you started. Small wonder that the better-organised mining concerns kept detailed plans of their mining excavations, which prove equally important to those hardy souls who are today investigating the old mine workings.

Lead

L ead is a material whose usefulness has long been recognised. Lead, symbol Pb (Latin *plumbum*, a lead weight), is a dense, bluish-grey metallic element that was one of the first known metals. However, as the more toxic properties have come to light, its reputation has become somewhat tarnished.

Lead was one of the first metal ores to be mined. Lead is widely distributed all over the world in the form of its sulphide, the ore galena, and ranks about 36th in natural abundance among elements in the earth's crust. Where lead-bearing veins were discovered near the surface (as in the Pennines), lead could be mined by even the most primitive methods. With its relatively low melting point, lead was also easy to smelt. Hundreds of years before the advent of purpose-built mills, lead ore was smelted in crude, open hearths.

Metallic lead is a soft, malleable, ductile metal. It has low tensile strength and is a poor conductor of electricity. A freshly cut surface has a bright silvery lustre, which quickly turns to the dull, bluish-grey colour characteristic of the metal. Lead's malleability – being easily worked, bent and shaped – made it particularly prized in building construction. The Romans used lead extensively for weatherproofing the roofs of their houses, and for making pipes, drains and cisterns. Lead still has its place in the building trade today, though increased awareness of its toxic qualities means we no longer consider it appropriate to use for drinking water pipes.

The Romans found other applications for lead – particularly in making paint pigments – and definitely mined lead during their occupation of Britain. Little lead was mined here for centuries after the Romans left. During the Middle Ages lead was used mainly for weatherproofing church roofs. The beautiful stained glass windows of our great cathedrals and churches could not have been made without the strips of lead that held each fragment of coloured glass in place. Molten lead was also poured into moulds to make bullets and musket balls.

Lead Mining in the Yorkshire Dales

The production of finer lead shot required a different technique and even a special building of unusual dimensions. The process, perfected during the 1780s, required the mixing of lead with a proportion of arsenic. When this mixture was forced through the perforations in a grid, hard, round droplets were formed. They were allowed to fall down, sometimes as far as 50 metres, into water. The droplets solidified during their descent, and the water prevented them from going out of shape on impact.

Mining remained sporadic (or at least poorly documented) until the sixteenth century: the time of 'the great rebuilding'. Wood-framed houses were being rebuilt, more substantially, in brick and stone. Successful merchants rewarded themselves with houses of substance to reinforce their new-found status in society. 'Old money' was used to build ever more stately homes for the aristocracy. Lead was a vital element – particularly as thatched roofs were being replaced by slates and tiles.

During the 17th, 18th and 19th centuries, lead mining became an increasingly important industry, with production raised to meet the needs of markets all around the globe. Britain was, for a long period, the world's biggest exporter of lead. At this time lead was in great demand for pipes, water cisterns, roofing, printers' type, lead shot, pewter and as an ingredient in paint and 'lead' crystal glass.

Significant finds were made throughout many of the country's upland areas, particularly the Pennines (from the Peak District up to Northumberland), the Lake District and Cornwall. Mines were also to be found in many Welsh counties, Dumfriesshire and Lanarkshire in Scotland, and the Isle of Man.

The decline of our lead mining industry did not reflect any decline in the demand for lead. Rather, cheap imports during the 19th century, especially from Spain and Australia, gradually eroded Britain's pre-eminence. From being the biggest net exporter of lead in the world, Britain was – by 1880 – a distant fourth, behind Spain, Germany and the United States. At the turn of the century most British mining concerns were either facing bankruptcy or turning their attentions elsewhere.

Lead

Twentieth-century mining for lead has been intermittent, in Britain at least. Particularly rich veins kept a few mines going, and many old spoil heaps have been reworked, using more efficient separation techniques. Lead has largely been won, however, as a by-product of mining other metals, such as barytes, calcite and fluorspar.

The worldwide demand for lead is now being met by modern mines in Australia, the United States and Canada. Current uses of lead mostly exploit its resistance to corrosion and its impermeability to X-rays. It has become a valuable material for covering electricity and telephone cables – especially those laid underground and underwater. Lead oxide (red lead) and the carbonate (white lead) are both paint bases.

Lead is used in enormous quantities in storage batteries and in sheathing electric cables. Large quantities are used in industry for lining pipes, tanks, and X-ray apparatus. Because of its high density and nuclear properties, lead is used extensively as protective shielding for radioactive material. A considerable amount of lead is consumed in the form of its compounds, particularly in paints and pigments.

A major application is for the plates of wet batteries, such as those found in cars. Tetraethyl lead has been an additive in petrol since the early days of motoring, introduced to give better engine performance. In these environmentally conscious times, however, leaded petrol is being supplanted by lead-free fuel, which offers cleaner exhaust emissions. Legislation has forced paint manufacturers, too, to phase out the use of lead in their products, largely owing to tragic incidents of children being poisoned.

Lead taken internally in any of its forms is highly toxic; the effects are usually felt after it has accumulated in the body over a period of time. The symptoms of lead poisoning are anaemia, weakness, constipation, colic, palsy, and often a paralysis of the wrists and ankles. Flaking lead-based paints and toys made from lead compounds are considered serious hazards for children. They are especially at risk from lead, even at levels once thought safe. Lead can reduce intelligence, delay motor development, impair memory, and cause hearing problems and troubles in balance. In adults, one lead hazard at levels once thought safe is that of increased blood pressure.

It has long been understood that lead – in all its compounds – is toxic, though this didn't stop it being used at various times for such unsuitable applications as water pipes, cosmetics and even – a chilling thought – to impart an artificial whiteness to our daily bread.

Prospecting

The lead mines of Yorkshire are to be found in the Pennine hills, an area roughly defined by the Yorkshire Dales National Park, plus Nidderdale. It is in these upland areas – typically at a height above sea level of between 300m and 600m – that the geology is conducive to the presence of lead ore. Here are to be found millstone grit and carboniferous limestone; fissures in these rocks were mineralised by the end of the Palaeozoic period (180 million years ago). They were filled with molten minerals, of which the most important was galena (lead sulphide). When cool these minerals crystallised into veins which vary greatly in thickness, from a few centimetres to a metre or more.

Lead, in the form of galena, is usually found in thin, vertical veins. They can, perhaps, best be imagined as walls buried in the ground. Horizontal deposits, known as 'flats', were less commonly encountered.

Veins do not consist of pure lead ore only; the galena content may be as little as 5 per cent. Other minerals included calcite, fluorspar and large quantities of barytes. The miners discarded these other minerals as having no commercial value, and it wasn't until the 20th century that they were mined (or recovered by reworking old spoil heaps). Small amounts of silver (seldom exceeding two ounces per ton of galena) were sometimes found. At these levels the silver content was not reckoned to be worth the effort and expense of refining.

Veins of lead ore typically occurred in limestone (less commonly in grit, and rarely in shales). There was no way of being sure how far a vein would extend; similarly, a vein might be wide in some places and narrow in others. These were unknown quantities for which no satisfactory yardstick was found. Thus it was that lead mining was always a very speculative venture, with no guarantee that years of work and capital investment would show a profit.

When a productive vein appeared to have run out, there was no

Lead Mining in the Yorkshire Dales

knowing whether it finished there, or whether it would reappear a few yards further on. Miners had to decide whether to press on, digging through unproductive ground in the hope of striking ore again, or to cut their losses and strike off in another direction altogether.

There was a fine line between success and failure. Many companies ploughed the last of their capital into mining dead grounds, to strike only bankruptcy. Yet stories are also told of miners who lit one last candle, and vowed to abandon their mine if they hadn't struck ore by the time the candle had burned down – and managed to hit paydirt with the very last shovelful. Small wonder that lead miners were notoriously superstitious, and set great store by omens and premonitions.

In Swaledale and Arkengarthdale, lead prospectors were generally allowed free access to unenclosed land – at least until the 17th century. If their initial prospecting proved fruitful, they would then have first option to mine there. Claims were often marked out by inscribed meer stones, a meer being a unit of measurement about 25 metres long. Landowners were equally keen to share in the profits engendered from land that might otherwise have been of little value. They would claim a royalty of between an eighth and a twelfth of any ore discovered.

Miners and prospectors kept trying to make their industry more reliant on science and less on chance, and collated the particular criteria that would promise a good vein. They learned much; nevertheless the certainty of finding riches always eluded them.

Most of the mines mentioned in this book belong to one of two major mining fields. The mines of Swaledale, Arkengarthdale and the north side of Wensleydale comprise one group. Another encompasses the mines around Greenhow Hill, in Nidderdale, and Grassington, in Wharfedale.

The mines of the northern Dales exploit a large number of veins, orientated roughly east-west. One of the most important is the Friarfold vein, which extends from Keld in the west to Arkengarthdale in the east. The Grassington-Greenhow field is dominated by the Bycliffe vein, which is nine miles long.

Prospecting

The Arkengarthdale mines exploited the Friarfold vein of lead. Langthwaite's two smelt mills are pictured in 1946. New Mill is in the foreground and Octagon Mill behind. Both are now demolished.

Dr J O Myers

Most of the major mining fields had been discovered by the 16th century. Finding individual veins came next. Prospecting tended to be rather unscientific, consisting of searching upland streams for traces of lead ore. The presence of even minute quantities might encourage further investigation.

Another useful clue to the presence of lead ore was the flora to be found growing in the vicinity. Many plants will not grow where lead is found; conversely there are a few species which thrive in this environment. The species which can tolerate the presence of lead in the soil are therefore valuable indicators for lead pollution. They would also have helped mining prospectors to pinpoint sites where further investigation might prove worthwhile. These plants include spring sandwort (also known as leadwort), scurvey grass, alpine penny cress, mountain pansy and moonwort.

The next step, typically, was hushing: allowing a torrent of water to rush down the hillside and perhaps expose a vein. Where veins outcropped they could be worked from the surface, requiring a minimum of digging. These were, naturally enough, the first veins to be exploited.

Mining Methods

Without venturing underground, it's hard for us to have a clear understanding about what life was really like for the lead miners of the Yorkshire Dales. But just peering a few yards into the dank darkness of a mining level can elicit a shudder.

Imagine: it's early in the morning, and you're stumbling into the blackness, with only a flickering candle flame to light your way. The candle may have burned down before you get to where you are working. It's winter, so it's dark when you enter the mine, and dark again when you emerge hours later, weary, wet and hungry. You see daylight only at the weekends.

Water rushes past, soaking your trousers; the level you stumble along also serves to drain the water away. You're not alone; every miner knows it's dangerous to go into a mine on his own.

You carry the tools of your trade, a pick and a shovel. You take good care of them; you are, after all, buying them from the mining agent. You feel, despite all evidence to the contrary, that you're going to have a lucky strike today.

Your clogs clatter along the rocky level. You are wearing the miner's 'uniform': corduroy trousers, shirt and waistcoat. The clothes are tight, which helps when you are moving through constricted parts of the level. Loose garments might catch on nail-heads or rough parts of the walls.

Hunger is kept at bay by your breakfast of oatmeal porridge and milk. You carry your mid-day meal – perhaps bread and cheese – and a tin bottle containing cold tea or water.

The arched entrance to a level is all that the visitor of today is likely to see. So the purpose of this chapter is to shine a little light into those dark recesses: to discover how the miners spent their working days underground.

The technical aspects of lead mining were slow to change, not least because the mines were a long way away from established centres of industry. It is best to provide a picture of those mining

Lead Mining in the Yorkshire Dales

practices that were common in the 18th and 19th centuries: that is, the era to which most surviving mining buildings belong.

From the earliest days the miners' tools were likely to have been picks and shovels – just as they still were at the end of the last century. By the time new mining techniques were available to meet the needs of the isolated Pennine mines, the price of the lead was being significantly undercut by imports.

There were two basic ways to reach lead-bearing veins: the vertical shaft driven down into a vein from above, or the level driven horizontally into (or parallel with) a vein from lower down. Certainly, during the 18th and 19th centuries both levels and shafts were used in the creation of an integrated mining system. Shafts were preferred on flat sites such as Grassington Moor. Where productive veins were intersected by steep-sided valleys (such as Hard Level and Gunnerside Gill) there would be a greater preponderance of levels.

Shafts were typically two metres or less in diameter, and usually stone-lined through unstable ground. They gave access to other areas of the mine, often by means of a wooden ladder mounted against one side of the shaft. Alternatively, there might be wooden steps, known as stemples, running across one end of the shaft. Stemples were reckoned to be less safe than ladders, as they were susceptible to rotting where they were let into the sides of the shaft.

The consequence of stepping onto a rotten stemple could be a serious accident or even a fatal fall. Ladders also took up less room, allowing the shaft to serve additionally for the removal of ore, waste and water from the mine. Some shafts were fitted, at intervals of a few yards, with wooden platforms. If a miner were to lose his footing his fall would soon be broken, thus preventing a fatal fall.

Ore and waste materials were raised to the surface in a bucket, known as a kibble, attached to the end of a rope. In shallow shafts the bucket would be raised by hand. In deeper shafts it would be drawn up using a simple windlass called a jack roller. This proved a laborious way of raising ore, deads and water from a mine; 'kibbling' could occupy as many man hours as were being spent in driving the levels underground.

Mining Methods

This method became untenable for deeper shafts. The weight of a very long rope would become too great for one man to lift. An elegant solution to this problem was a device known as a horse whim, or gin. This was basically a more sophisticated version of the jack-roller, but turned on its side and operated by one horse (or sometimes two, in harness). Horse whims were to be found in the Yorkshire Dales mining fields by the closing years of the 17th century, and continued to the end of the mining era.

A horse walked in a circle, around a thick wooden post. The bottom of this post tapered to a point, ending in an iron spike, which was able to turn freely in a hollowed-out rock. The post was mounted to rotate against a cross-arm, which was supported at either end by end-posts. This woodwork merely served as a solid frame, within which the centre post could turn freely.

The horse turned the centre post and, along with it, a large drum, around which the rope was wound or unwound. This action was sufficient to bring a laden kibble to the surface. A pair of kibbles could be worked by a single horse whim – one kibble coming up as the other was going down. Leading a horse around and around the whim was the first task at the mines that many a young lad would perform.

Horse whims, being made mainly of wood, did not survive long after the mines were abandoned. No examples can be seen today in the Yorkshire Dales mining fields. All that remains are a few flat circles on the ground, adjacent to the shafts, showing where the whims once stood. Such traces can be found on Grassington Moor and on some of the higher ground in Arkengarthdale.

A two-horse whim provided an efficient lifting system, and horses were typically harnessed for shifts of between three and six hours. Lifting ore was not a continuous process; it depended on what was happening underground. Draining the water from a mine was, on the other hand, a job that – if it needed to be done at all – needed to be done continuously. Teams of horses might operate, in shifts, right around the clock.

When shafts were sunk to great depths (100 metres and more were not unknown), horse power alone was unequal to the task of bringing ore to the surface. During the 18th and 19th centuries this was one of the many processes for which waterwheels were harnessed. One problem, on flatter sites at least, was finding a dependable source of water, since the mining fields with the most shafts tended to be those, like Grassington Moor, without fast-flowing becks.

Horse whims were particularly inefficient at draining water from the mines, so the mining concerns went to a good deal of trouble and expense to bring water to turn the wheels. They created complex systems of watercourses; they made reservoirs; they dammed existing lakes; in short they tried to ensure a good head of water at most times of the year.

It was ironic that water was both the problem and the solution. Even more ironic was the fact that mines were most likely to flood during dry periods, when there might not be a sufficient force of water to operate the pumps.

The driving of levels served the same basic purpose as the sinking of shafts: to reach a productive, ore-bearing vein as quickly and efficiently as possible. Levels are associated with those mining fields in which valleys and ravines cut across the veins, such as in Swaledale and Arkengarthdale. Where veins occurred near the surface, the usual way of reaching it was by hushing.

It is no accident that many levels were driven through the base of hushes and into the hillsides. Veins usually occurred in the vertical plane and, when hushing became uneconomic, a level might be driven to exploit the same vein from lower down. The miners could be fairly confident that their labours would be rewarded. Sometimes, however, their explorations broached older workings. Many a miner was to find that 'the old man' (their evocative expression for miners of earlier times) had been there before.

Like shafts, levels were built to accomplish various tasks. They offered miners a route to the mine-head that didn't involve climbing. Though most would have to stoop for part of the way, the men could at least walk into the mine. Such levels would typically be less than two metres high, and one metre wide. The entrance to the level would

Mining Methods

Levels are associated with mining fields in which valleys and ravines cut across the veins of lead. This is Stang Level, Faggergill Mine, Arkengarthdale, circa 1910.

J Backhouse

usually be built of dressed stone, in a simple arch shape, and the level would continue in these approximate dimensions until it opened out into mine workings, or branched off into other levels or shafts.

Horse levels were both higher and wider (2.2 metres by 1.3 metres was typical), to allow easy access for the Dales Galloway ponies used to haul waggons in and out of the mines. Also associated with these levels are narrow gauge railways, along which waggons were pushed and pulled. First made of wood, the rails were generally upgraded, in the early years of the 19th century, to more durable cast and wrought iron. While there was no standard shape for waggons, most were about 75cm wide, 1.2m high and up to 2m long.

The rails would be extended underground as required, by adding

Lead Mining in the Yorkshire Dales

further rails, to reach the mine head. Some of these subterranean railway systems were remarkably complex. For example, it was said that there were twenty-five miles of rails in the Faggergill mines. On emerging into the daylight, the rails would usually continue to the bouseteams, stone containers into which each mining partnership would store their bouse before it was dressed and washed in preparation for smelting.

There was a third, equally important, reason for driving a level: to drain the mine. Water was the bane of the miner's life: one of the principal reasons why mines had to be abandoned. Levels, despite the name, were driven at a slight uphill incline. This served a dual purpose: making it easier to bring laden tubs out of the mine, and allowing water to flow freely away. Many miners would have arrived at their place of work with wet feet, but this was seen as a small price to pay for keeping floodwater out of the workings.

Another good reason for driving a level – rather than sinking a shaft from above – was to increase the chances of hitting a vein other than the one being sought. As ore-bearing veins occurred vertically, as a rule, a vertical shaft was unlikely to uncover new strata.

The driving of levels was an expensive business, though the costs were spread out over the years of excavation. Another problem was the slow progress. The narrowness of the typical level meant that there would have been room for just two or three men at a time to work. Picks and shovels were supplemented, from the middle of the 18th century, by the use of gunpowder.

Even when tunnelling was undertaken round-the-clock, progress was often painfully slow. It wasn't merely that the financial outlay had to be recouped, more that it might be years before that could even begin. Gunpowder helped to speed up tunnelling, though the mining companies of the Yorkshire Dales were slow to adopt other, less labour intensive, methods.

The Sir Francis Level, in Gunnerside Gill, was an exception. Begun in 1864, to provide a new approach into the productive Friarfold vein, the level had advanced by only 400 metres during the first five years of excavation. It was at this point that the mining

The Sir Francis lead mine (above) in Gunnerside Gill and its bousteams (below). Construction of the level here broke new ground, with the use of dynamite and rock boring equipment speeding up the work.

Bunton is one of three massive hushes in Gunnerside Gill. Hushing use

e action of running water to remove loose material lying over lead veins.

The smelt mill at the Grinton lead mine. The historical importance of such sites is now being recognised and restoration undertaken.

Mining Methods

company brought in dynamite and the very latest rock boring equipment, which was powered by compressed air. The result was the completion of the level in a third of the time (and half the cost) that could have been accomplished by pick and shovel alone.

Mechanical rock borers became commonplace in Yorkshire mines from the 1870s. These developments speeded up the tunnelling process, but came too late to alter significantly the fortunes of the lead mining industry, which was by this time in terminal decline.

Levels could be driven much faster by using gunpowder, but there was a price to pay. Setting off a charge filled the air with dust and smoke; miners seldom waited for the air to clear before taking up their picks and shovels again. Nor was it unknown for accidents to occur with the setting of the explosives.

Easily worked veins were tackled with hammer, pick and shovel. To split rock faces, the miners used simple devices called plugs and feathers. Plugs were narrow, wedge-shaped chisels, which fitted snugly inside the feathers, a pair of shaped metal surrounds. Once a hole large enough to accommodate these feathers had been made into the rock, the plug could be hammered in between them, splitting the rock further apart with each successive blow.

After the introduction of explosives, miners confronted by harder ground might prefer to blast their way through. For the explosives to have maximum effect, they needed to be confined within the rock, rather than just dissipate into the surrounding air.

Holes were made by hammering a pointed, chisel-shaped iron drill, known as a jumper, into the rock: a wearisome job. Into the hole was slid a narrow cartridge of gunpowder. A thin rod (known as a needle or pricker) was carefully pushed into this paper cartridge, creating a hole into which a fuse could be inserted. Sometimes iron prickers would create sparks off the surrounding rock, and set off the explosive prematurely. Following a number of tragic accidents, an Act of Parliament was passed, determining that these tools be made of copper or other non-ferrous metal.

Once the fuse was lit the men would move swiftly to a position of safety. After the explosion they went back to work with their picks and shovels, clearing away the blasted rock. This process might be repeated a number of times each day, causing the men to spend the whole of a shift labouring in a dusty haze.

There was always an element of unpredictability in the use of explosives. A blast might go off too quickly, or cause a roof-fall. Even when the blasts went according to plan, the constant inhalation of fumes and dust contributed to the lung diseases that brought the working lives of so many lead miners to a premature end.

Where levels were being driven through solid rock, there was no need to support the roof. But when levels passed through friable material and loose rock, the roofs would be reinforced with dressed stone to create the familiar, self-supporting, arched profile. A cheaper – but less permanent – option was to use wooden supports.

By the late 18th century, the easily worked veins in the main mining fields were mostly exhausted. Lead ore had to be harder won, with deeper shafts and longer levels being driven to exploit lower areas of ore-bearing vein. To reach productive areas of the main veins, greater and greater distances had to be broached. A miner might stumble through his subterranean warren for perhaps an hour before he reached the mine-head.

Driving tunnels through dead ground represented quite a leap of faith on behalf of a mining company, as there was no way of knowing how far a vein might extend in any direction. A cross-cut was a level that was driven to link two other levels, or to prospect for another vein. We can envisage the mines as complex arrangements of interconnecting shafts, levels and cross-cuts. In the major mining fields north of the River Swale, these underground workings extended a great distance.

Mines belonging to more than one company might be linked together. This arrangement might work to mutual advantage, allowing, for example, a drainage level to unwater more than one mine. Conversely, it could cause wrangles by creating the possibility of sabotage. During the protracted legal battles that beset the Yorkshire mines it was not unknown for miners to flood another company's mine, or block up access.

Mining Methods

Sturdy mining tubs were used to bring hard-won lead to the surface.

Once they had entered the mine – whether by shaft or level, or a combination of the two – miners would make their way to the mine-head, where the ore itself was won. While there was no single way of working a vein, a few practices were general.

Miners traditionally worked upwards into a vein, a process known as overhand stoping. This allowed the deads and rubble to drop down and away from the workings. The men dug into the vein with picks and shovels, loading the more promising material into a waggon or kibble. The workings were usually widened to accommodate a primitive railway system.

Once they had worked out that portion of the vein in front of them, the miners would build a wooden platform to stand upon. From this new height the miners could continue to win ore from the vein. This process might be repeated many times, with timber staging and ladders scaling the vein, until the miners were working at a considerable height above their original level. If the vein proved rich in ore, it might be considered worthwhile to drive another level – higher up, or perhaps lower down – in the hope that the vein would continue to be workable.

When the miners had to work down into a vein (underhand stoping), they created what was known as a sump. If the vein was in the form of a flat (an uncommon occurrence), the miners would branch out sideways, using wooden posts to shore up the roof and prevent rock-falls.

The precious galena was brought to the surface; the problem was what to do with the 'deads'. It was considered good mining practice to bring this out too, and only to dump the deads underground in those worked-out areas that were never going to be explored again. These good intentions were not always realised, however, as the disposing of deads could be regarded as an unproductive task: that is, one that used up time and energy without winning any ore.

Underground railways helped in the transport of ore and deads out of the mine, but there was still a great deal of back-breaking manual labour involved. Bouse might have to be carried in buckets or barrows from the mine head to the waggons – perhaps being winched up a number of sumps or shafts in the process. Every waggon load of ore was won only with the greatest of effort.

Bailey J Harker, author of *Rambles in Upper Wharfedale* in 1869, provided a vivid description of life down the mines. This extract refers to a visit to the Grassington mines: "It is very interesting to strangers to enter them, though perhaps the descent may frighten them a little. The bottom of some of the shafts is reached by ladders, and others by ropes. When you are safely down you will be led by one of the miners into the different 'levels', holding in your hand a candle in a piece of clay, to keep your hand from melting the tallow by its warmth.

"At the first it will prove curious work for you, sometimes to be climbing up ladders then rambling over rocks, then wading through water, then marching through mud, then creeping through holes; at times clambering up a narrow bore, hobbling along a narrow passage, squeezing through a tortuous crevice; then going on all fours, bear fashion, crawling, scrambling, struggling along the subterranean recesses, from which the precious ore has been dug. But to see the rich veins of lead 'glinting and sparkling like jewels in the rock', and the 'little caverns of spar' – 'glittering grottos of well-defined crystal' – that 'sparkle like fairy halls', or 'miniature palaces of pearl, spangled with more than oriental splendour', will give pleasure that will more than reward you for your toil."

Dressing

Dressing was a term used by the lead miners for the various processes by which the bouse material extracted from the mines was brought to a condition suitable for smelting. What emerged from out of the levels, trundled in the characteristically narrow waggons, drawn by men or pit ponies, was a mixture of rock, lead ore and other minerals. Lead ore typically constituted a mere 5 per cent of these loads, though a particularly rich seam might yield a greater percentage.

Dressing floors were clearly defined areas – often stone-flagged, sometimes open to the elements – where ore was broken down. They were usually sited close to (and slightly downhill from) the entrance to a mining level. This minimised the distance that bouse would have to be transported; as soon as smeltable ore was separated from the waste, the latter could be tipped onto a nearby spoil heap. Some dressing floors are now so dilapidated that these spoil heaps offer the only visible clues as to their whereabouts.

It was also advantageous to site dressing floors close to running water: a free-flowing river or beck. Many becks were polluted and discoloured by the work carried out on these dressing floors. Water was needed for many of the dressing processes, and turned the waterwheels that were harnessed to power crushing rollers and hammers. If a convenient source of water wasn't available, a spring or stream might be diverted.

Enormous energy might be expended in creating dams, artificial water-courses, leats, launders and aqueducts – to ensure an unfailing water supply to a dressing floor. Whenever miners had disputes, water and its availability was one of the commonest causes. Indeed, the shortage of water, and the expense of diverting it, encouraged many mining operations to share the use of a dressing floor.

The principle underpinning most of the dressing processes is simple: the difference in density between rock and lead ore. Pure lead ore (galena) has a higher specific gravity than the other mined

Dressing

materials (7.5 for galena, less than 4 for the 'deads'). When riddled in water, bouse separates out, the ore sinking to the bottom much quicker than other materials.

During the 16th and 17th centuries the dressing processes were done – laboriously – by hand. As the 18th century dawned some of these processes began to be mechanised, powered by huge water-wheels. Bouse was broken up by mechanical crushers, instead of being hammered by hand. This same water power was used to automate the previously labour-intensive tasks of sieving and buddling. At the height of the industry there were more than a hundred water wheels operating in the Yorkshire Dales mining fields.

A compact mining field typically comprised a number of features. There would be a level, or levels, out of which waggons of bouse were dragged. Stone compartments or hoppers, known as bouseteams, accommodated the bouse mined by each partnership. By counting the number of bays in a bouseteam, we can get a good idea of the number of mining teams working a particular mine.

The bouse was taken from the bouseteam to the nearby dressing floor for crushing and sieving. When lead ore was sufficiently pure and ground small enough, it was ready for smelting. The smelt mill might be a few yards away; in mining fields where one mill served a number of different mines the distance might be a mile or more.

If you examine the entrance to some of the low-level adits, you may find rusty iron rails leading away from the mine. This was the miners' primitive railway, used for bringing bouse to the surface. If you follow the rails – or can at least trace where they once went – you may find they lead directly to a nearby bouseteam, at a height level with the top of the hoppers. This allowed bouse to be tipped directly into the bouseteams. A good example of this arrangement can be seen at the restored Beldi Hill dressing floor in Swaledale (alas, with no public access at the time of writing).

If it was the miners who manhandled most of the bouse out of the mine, it was more likely to be boys, women and older men who worked the bouse on the dressing floor. They would rake out bouse from the bouseteams, and roughly sort it by hand.

Lead Mining in the Yorkshire Dales

Lumps of pure galena were transferred to a pile; it could be taken straight to the smelt mill. 'Deads' containing no ore were discarded and would find their way to a nearby spoil heap. When galena and other minerals were lumped together, the lead ore would be knocked off with a spalling hammer.

Irregular pieces of galena were now reduced in size by use of a bucker (a short, heavy hammer with a squared-off iron head), usually on a stone-flagged area of the dressing floor. This primitive method of breaking up the bouse was, not surprisingly, one of the first dressing processes to be mechanised. A waterwheel could outperform a whole gang of boys, by transferring power to a crusher or stamper.

Crushing engines can best be imagined as outsized mangles, with a pair of heavy iron rollers mounted in parallel. Typically the rollers would rotate in opposite directions – that is, towards the gap between them – with one roller fixed in place and the other allowed to 'give' a little. This meant the rollers could crush different sizes of bouse with ease. Efficient crushers could reduce bouse to the consistency of fine gravel.

Crushing hammers performed a similar task, but with a different action. Heavy cubes of stone were lifted and dropped in turn onto piles of bouse. This method of crushing ore-rich material was less common, at least in the Yorkshire Dales.

The result was much the same, whether the ore was broken up by bucker, roller or crusher, though mechanisation allowed for a much faster throughput of ore to feed the smelt mills. Mechanisation was never more than partial, and manual labour was still required for shovelling bouse through the rollers or under the hammers.

With bouse reduced to small granules of roughly uniform size, other processes could be brought into play, using the different densities of ore and rock to separate them out. One simple method was to push a sieve of bouse up and down in a tub of water. This action – known as jigging – left concentrated galena at the bottom of the sieve, while lighter waste materials would settle on top and were then easily discarded.

This sieving action was replicated more efficiently in hotching

Dressing

Bunton crushing wheel, Gunnerside Gill. Such wheels were used to reduce the mined lead to the consistency of fine gravel.

tubs, the sieving action being accomplished by means of a long lever arm. The operator stood well clear of the splashing water, and activated the sieve by jigging the lever up and down. A hotching tub could treat a load about five times as big as could be sieved by hand. Later versions of the hotching tub were adapted to work from a waterwheel: they were known as 'self-active jiggers'.

Material finer than that riddled in the hotching tub was subjected to a gentler flow of water, in a device known as a buddle. Fine ore – 'slimes' in the mining vernacular – was not allowed to escape. Instead it was 'buddled': washed in a gentle stream of water and raked by the operator. The lighter waste material was washed away, leaving the heavier ore behind.

Running buddles separated larger particles, leaving the finer slimes to be sorted in a trunk buddle. A stepped design allowed the operator to rake the slimes in a continuous flow of water. Lighter waste would be carried away with the water flow.

Lead Mining in the Yorkshire Dales

Most buddles – like the hotching tubs – were generally made of wood, and only traces have survived. This is why a trip to a working museum such as Killhope is invaluable, with so many of these processes and devices being faithfully recreated for 'hands-on' use by visitors.

The circular (or 'centre head') buddle was generally a more permanent structure. A good example can be found at the Stoney Grooves dressing floor on the Greenhow Hill mining field. What you can see now is a flat, sunken circle bordered by a double layer of dressed stone. In use there would have been a wooden frame, stretched across the middle of the buddle, supporting a spindle around which a wooden paddle rotated. This paddle would have been driven by a waterwheel.

Slimes and water were deposited by a leat into the centre of the buddle. The action of the water and the paddle spread the slimes around the buddle – the pure galena being deposited near the centre, and lighter waste running off towards the sides.

These methods were gradually improved throughout the years that lead was mined in the Yorkshire Dales. Some ideas came from further afield. The circular buddle, for example, was more commonly found in Cornish mines. All the buddles were, in any case, merely refinements on the age-old practice of sieving rock in running water, when panning for gold and other precious metals: a process familiar to aficionados of cowboy films.

The last line of defence, on many dressing floors, was the slime pit where, after riddling, jigging, hotching and buddling, a fine sludge was all that remained. It was vital to recover as much galena as possible from every tub of mined ore, considering the great effort expended to win it from the mines. Nevertheless, when efforts have been made, in more recent years, to glean lead ore from the old mine workings, the most profitable course of action has generally been the reworking of the spoil heaps.

Despite the miners' best efforts, and even after all the processes undertaken on the dressing floor, there was a percentage of ore left in the piles of deads. It was worthwhile for people to go through these

Dressing

spoil heaps, to recover even this small amount of lead; after all, they did not have the labour and expense of mining it.

This reworking of old spoil heaps continued long after the mining had stopped. New advances in mineral technology have allowed successive generations of entrepreneurs to salvage ore from waste material.

Mills

The lead mines of the Yorkshire Dales have changed little since they were abandoned in the latter years of the last century. A few relics – waggons, tools, etc. – have been recovered and removed to museums. The levels have mostly been left alone.

The smelt mills, however, and the other buildings associated with the processing of galena into lead ingots, have received more attention – not least from builders. The chapel at Muker, for example, was built from dressed stone salvaged from the Old Gang Smelt Mill. Other mills have succumbed to the sort of vandalism that cannot resist the urge to break down what others have built up. We have the Army to thank for using the Kettlewell Smelt Mill for target practice.

Most of the smelt mills stopped working a century ago. The decision whether to repair, or to let fall into ruin, has largely been based on whether or not a building might have been useful to the landowner. This hit-or-miss attitude to conservation reflects the fact that an interest in our industrial heritage is a relatively recent development.

Hindsight is always 20:20 vision, of course, and it's perhaps too easy to voice regret that more has not been done to maintain the fabric of the most interesting mills and mining fields. We can look at the foundations of the great Octagon Mill, at Langthwaite, and wish there had been restoration rather than demolition, or wonder what the Old Gang mining complex might look like today if consolidation work had been started a few years earlier.

Where there *has* been consolidation work, as at Grinton Smelt Mill or the Beldi Hill dressing floor, visitors can get a much clearer picture of how the lead ore was mined, dressed and smelted. Even fewer mining buildings survive at the Weardale mines, to the north of the Yorkshire Dales, which makes the survival and subsequent restoration of the Killhope complex particularly important. Considering the number of lead mining sites in the Dales, a similar Yorkshire venture would surely attract large numbers of visitors.

Mills

One of the reasons why lead has been mined in Britain since the Roman occupation – if not before – is the metal's relatively low melting point. The Romans smelted lead in small stone hearths, with a draught provided by foot-operated bellows.

The technology of smelting cannot be said to have greatly advanced during the twelve centuries following the Romans' departure. Generations of mining adventurers smelted their galena on exposed hillsides, known as bail hills. The word 'bail' (and many other variants) may derive from the Norse word 'bal', meaning a fire.

Sites were typically chosen for being exposed to the full force of the prevailing winds. A crude, circular furnace was constructed from stone, with openings left near the bottom to funnel the wind into the heart of the fire. The inside was usually lined with clay, in a bowl shape, with a channel created for the molten lead to run off into a collecting vessel.

Inside the furnace, layers of galena would be alternated with layers of fuel: likely to be wood, peat or coal (when available). When lit in a strong, steady wind, the fire would heat up the galena sufficiently to smelt it into 'pigs' of lead.

The only improvement made to this rudimentary method was to create a strong, regulated draught by hand-operated bellows, instead of waiting for the wind to blow. This naturally dispensed with the need to use an exposed and windswept site. Today, little more than the names live on; look out on large-scale maps for names that include 'bale', 'bail', 'baill', 'baal' and 'bole'. Traces of these crude hearths themselves (and the slag that remained) have been found near Pateley Bridge, on Winterings Scar overlooking Gunnerside Gill and at other sites in the northern Dales.

German miners brought more advanced mining and smelting techniques to Britain during the mid-16th century. Instead of having to rely on a compliant wind blowing from one particular direction, they devised purpose-built ore hearths and powered their bellows with a more controllable source of power: water.

Smelt mills gradually replaced boles during the second half of the 16th century, once William Humphrey had patented a method of smelting ore by means of furnace and bellows. The earliest purpose-built smelt mills in the Yorkshire Dales for which records are known were at Marske (built in 1588) and Marrick (1592).

The need for a constant supply of water – rather than a strong wind – meant that the miners looked to the valleys rather than exposed hill-tops. Thus it was that smelt mills came to be sited beside one of the many rivers or becks that flowed through the mining fields. The mining companies were not averse to diverting streams and building dams, to ensure a good head of water for turning the waterwheels.

Ore hearths were, in their most basic form, not dissimilar to a blacksmith's forge. The hearth was usually built of cast iron, to a height of a metre or more. An aperture at the back of the hearth accommodated the nozzle of the bellows, so that air could be forced directly into the base of the fire.

Once the fire had been brought up to operating temperature (about 600 to 800 degrees Centigrade), the ore was added. The fierce heat drove the sulphur from the ore; as it melted, the lead trickled down through the fire and into the cast iron hearth. The molten lead was directed along a channel and into a pre-heated cast iron container known as a sumpter pot. From here the lead could be transferred to cast iron moulds.

Fuel could generally be found close at hand. Until the end of the 17th century, kiln-dried wood was the principal fuel to fire the furnaces. Many woods in the Yorkshire Dales area were coppiced to provide 'chopwood' for the smelt mills. As mining and smelting became industrialised, the demand for wood began to outstrip the supply. When wood became scarce, and therefore more expensive to buy and transport, the smelters turned to peat as a source of fuel. Open-sided buildings for storing peat are often to be found adjacent to the smelt mills.

Packhorse trains may have brought coal from the mines of South Durham. Coal of poorer quality came across the moors to the smelt mills of Swaledale and Arkengarthdale from the collieries at Tan Hill. However, transport costs meant that the price of coal at the mill might be as much as three times the price at the colliery.

Mills

Northern Mines Records

Smelt mills smelted lead ore using a furnace enlivened by bellows. This is the Kettlewell Mill in Wharfedale, circa 1942.

The smelting process generated the poisonous fumes of sulphur dioxide, along with a small amount of lead oxide vapour. These fumes were harmful both to the men who worked in the mills and to any farm animals grazing in the vicinity. Vegetation, too, grew sparsely in ground that was particularly toxic.

In recognising the dangers, the miners tried to put as much distance as possible between themselves and these poisonous emissions. The favoured method was to build long, ground-level flues. Flues had other benefits. They provided a powerful draught that would boost the temperature of the furnaces. They also allowed the recovery of some of the lead oxide which might otherwise be lost in the fumes.

These aims were best achieved by making the flues as long as possible. Since the mills were usually sited at beck side, it became

51

usual (from the early 1800s) to build flues directly uphill from the mill. Flues can be found which extend a kilometre or more, ending in a more conventional stone chimney.

Most of those chimneys (some square in section, some round) are now in ruins. Those that didn't fall down have generally been demolished. Fortunately, two chimneys have been saved from this ignominious fate and still stand proud and tall – one on Grassington Moor, another on Malham Moor.

Many flues, too, have collapsed, though some fine examples can still be found at Grinton Mill, Grassington Moor, Old Gang Mill, and elsewhere. Flues were formed by digging out the route of the flue, arching over with stone, and creating an airtight finish by covering with turf. The result is a tunnel of such a height – 1 to 1.5 metres – that a man could walk through, albeit bent double.

The lead oxide vapour cooled as it ascended the flue and formed sooty deposits on the walls. The lead content of these deposits was sufficient to make it worthwhile to clean the flues from time to time. While water was being diverted down the length of the flue, boys would scrape the soot off the walls. These deposits would be washed down into settling pits near the mill. The work was as dangerous as it was dirty.

Sometimes a condenser would be built at some point along the flue's length (often lined with brushwood), to help the fine fumes of lead ore settle more readily. A double condenser can still be seen near the top of the flue from the Cupola Smelt Mill on Grassington Moor.

Most of the smelt mills to be seen in the Yorkshire Dales were built during a hundred year period between 1750 and 1850. The buildings are practical, with function to the fore, and designed to take advantage of their individual settings. Though they differ greatly in shape, size and arrangement they do have a few features in common. The presence of a long flue is very usual, though the precipitous siting of some mills (such as those at Blakethwaite and Beldi Hill) made the building of a flue quite an achievement.

The mills were fitted out with ore hearths – not unlike the more familiar blacksmith's hearth. These have, alas, all now disappeared,

The chimney and flue of Cupola Mill, Grassington Moor. This is a rare example of a chimney which has not either fallen or been demolished.

Old Gang smelt mill, Swaledale. This impressive site is one of fi

...ills in the Dales designated Scheduled Ancient Monuments.

The Blakethwaite smelt mill in Gunnerside Gill (above) and the High Winding Dam and Cupola Mill chimney on Grassington Moor (below).

though a pair of impressive furnace arches are still standing at Marrick Mill in Swaledale. A by-product of the smelting process was 'slag': impure lead oxide which floated to the top of the molten lead. Discarded in earlier times as waste, this slag was often re-smelted (at least in the larger mills) to reclaim some of its lead content.

Special slag hearths were built, which were designed to operate at higher temperatures than the ore hearths. This was to remove the oxygen from the lead oxide. Nevertheless, the lead that resulted was not of premium quality, and was often poured into moulds bearing the word 'Slagg'.

Pure molten lead, on the other hand, was poured into moulds bearing the mining company's name 'embossed' in reverse. The lettering was thus transferred to each pig of lead, ensuring that each ingot's provenance was beyond doubt. An additional code of letters could be added, to identify a batch of ingots. Examples of these cast iron moulds can be seen at the museums listed at the end of this book.

In addition to the ore hearth and slag hearth, a third kind of hearth came into use. Known as the roasting furnace, its purpose was mainly to consolidate very fine galena particles, and remove a percentage of the sulphur, so as to make it easier to smelt, later, in the ore hearth. The roasting furnace at the Old Gang Mill is to be found in a small, square building, separate from the rest of the mill, still topped by a distinctive and well-preserved chimney.

The reverberatory furnace was developed around 1700 by the London Lead Company. It enabled smelting to be developed on a larger, more efficient and truly industrial scale. The reverberatory furnace differed from the traditional ore hearth in that the ore did not come into direct contact with the fuel. The ore and fire were in separate chambers. The flames from the furnace were deflected – or 'reverberated' – beneath a curved roof and down onto the ore, thus bringing it up to smelting temperature.

This kind of furnace is associated with larger mills. Many reverberatory furnaces were designed for continuous running, and thus needed a constant supply of ore. They were often used to smelt the galena of more than one mining partnership.

Lead Mining in the Yorkshire Dales

A feature common to almost every mill was the presence of a waterwheel to drive the bellows. None of the smelt mills in the Yorkshire Dales still boasts a wheel 'in situ'. To see one in full working order you should make a trip to see the Killhope Mine in Weardale. Killhope's wheel was actually built to drive ore-crushing machinery in a dressing plant, rather than to power bellows. At more than 10 metres in diameter, it is an awesome sight, though wheels of similar size were once found throughout the Yorkshire Dales – to judge by the dimensions of the waterwheel pits that can still be found.

Transport

The Romans left many tangible reminders of a time when Britain was but a distant outpost of the Roman Empire. Their road system, for example, is a lasting monument to Roman ingenuity, forward planning and an overriding desire to keep the native Britons in their place.

It is likely that the Roman road between the forts at Aldborough and Ilkley (*Olicana* to the Romans) was built with the lead mines of Greenhow Hill in mind. It was here that the Romans established a mining field, perhaps using as slave labour some of the Brigantians they had captured in battle.

The routes across Stainmore, to the north of the Yorkshire Dales, and the Aire gap to the south, were consolidated by the Romans for the ease of moving their troops to quell local uprisings.

Since the Roman occupation the Dales have been mined for lead and, to a lesser extent, other minerals such as zinc, copper and iron. Limestone, too, has long been used to 'sweeten' poor upland soil. Coal was needed both for domestic use and as fuel to power the smelt mills. Stone was cut from quarries and transported for building purposes. The result was that a complex tracery of roads and tracks developed to cater for this ever-increasing traffic.

Some of these old thoroughfares have been upgraded by degrees into the metalled roads we know today. Others, especially those whose original purpose has long been forgotten, exist only on old maps, or as 'green lanes', or perhaps just the vaguest of lines still discernible in the landscape.

One feature common to all the lead mines is the complex pattern of tracks that link different parts of the mining sites with one another, and the mine complex with places further afield. These tracks offer an interesting insight into mining practice; many are public footpaths and bridleways which offer excellent walking for ramblers today.

From monastic times until the building of the turnpike roads, the standard method of transporting goods was by packhorse. Typically carrying a weight of more than 100kg, distributed in pannier bags hung on either side of the saddle, the horses would walk in single file. These 'trains' of horses and ponies were a common sight throughout the Dales. They were often heard even before they were seen, as the leading horse in each train would carry bells on its harness, to keep the horses together and announce their approach. Packhorses were able to negotiate the tracks of the Dales, most of them too rough for any kind of wheeled vehicle to use.

These horses often came from Germany, where they were known as Jaegers. This was corrupted by Dales accents into 'Jagger', a name also extended to the men who took charge of the packhorse trains. The word survives today in the name of many old tracks and as a surname.

The carriers – of lead and other goods – were usually independent operators, not in the employ of the mining companies. They would keep a stable of sturdy horses for hire by the load; while the mines were in full production they had regular work transporting ore and fuel to the smelt mills and pigs of lead to towns and ports. Some carriers were local farmers who kept horses as a sideline.

Lead from the northern Dales typically went to Richmond, Stockton or Yarm, situated on a bend in the River Tees. At Stockton and Yarm, agents were on hand to supervise the shipments of lead by sea. From the mines in the southern Dales, packhorse trains would carry lead ingots to Boroughbridge, Pateley Bridge, Skipton or Ripon.

By 1760 there were transport problems at the Grassington Moor mines – brought about, ironically, by the success of the enterprise. Lead output was growing too fast for the packhorse trains to handle. In any case many of the tracks were in poor condition, turning to mud in wet weather. The worst tracks were unusable in winter.

The cost of many other goods was artificially high, simply due to the costs of transport by a method as inefficient as packhorse trains. Costs commonly rose during the winter months because journeys took longer.

Lead from the Grassington Moor mines totalled 600 tons during

Transport

1760. It would have required about 6,000 individual journeys by packhorse to transport this tonnage from the smelt mills to Skipton or Pateley Bridge. This was in addition to the great number of shorter horse journeys required to take ore from dressing floor to mill. This traffic was supplemented by that required to transport fuel (mainly coal, wood and peat) for the smelt mills, and dressed stone and wood for work underground. The jaggers must have been a very familiar sight indeed.

The horses for this carriage work had to be fed, watered and stabled. The workload increased year by year, adding fuel to the argument that what the general transport system needed most of all was a radical overhaul.

The first Turnpike Act, in 1663, was concerned with the repairing of a section of the Great North Road, and the charging of tolls to pay for the work. By the beginning of the 18th century many more turnpike roads were being built, on similar principles: that those who needed to use the roads should be the ones to pay for their building and maintenance. The capital for these ventures came from the pockets of turnpike trustees, who were usually local landowners and business people.

All over Yorkshire turnpike trusts were set up. The rationale, reasonably enough, was that roads could earn money, instead of being a drain on the finances of the parishes through which they passed. The turnpike roads were generally made to link market towns and centres of industry. Goods could be transported more cheaply by wheeled vehicles of various types, chiefly because, load for load, only about half the number of horses were required, as compared with the packhorse trains.

The merchants of Yorkshire knew it was to their own benefit to upgrade the road system, and were therefore in the vanguard of subscribers to the turnpike trusts. Some of these subscribers also had business interests in the lead mines.

The Yorkshire Dales had presented many barriers to travel. The roads were notoriously bad: dusty and rock-strewn in summer, impassably boggy during the long winters.

Lead Mining in the Yorkshire Dales

The Grassington to Pateley Bridge turnpike was well used by carters taking lead away from the mines and then, on the return trip, loading up with coal to keep the smelt mill furnaces burning. The toll-house at Craven Cross levied tolls which depended on the number of horses pulling the carriage. A one-horse cart was levied 6d, while a four-horse waggon had to pay 1/10d. Coal carriers enjoyed preferential rates, a one-horse coal cart being charged only 1d.

The next significant change in the transport infrastructure of the southern Dales was the cutting of the Leeds-Liverpool Canal. By 1777 it had reached Gargrave, quite close to the mining fields of Grassington Moor. Gargrave and Skipton had wharves for the loading and unloading of goods, and it was not long before the canal was taking a good deal of mining traffic: lead out and coal in.

The railway reached Skipton in 1845, but the spur linking Skipton and Grassington wasn't opened until 1902: too late to help the lead miners. A Swaledale line, too, had once been mooted, though Richmond, in 1846, was as far into the dale as it ever reached. From this date the foremost destination for lead was Richmond railway station. A map of this proposed route can be viewed in the Richmondshire Museum in Richmond.

Miners

Life for the lead miners of the Yorkshire Dales was precarious – in every sense of the word. Whether working for themselves, or for one of the many companies to venture into the mining business, the work was hard, the rewards few and the future always uncertain. Lead mining was also a speculative venture, attracting its share of chancers and crooks, adventurers and cock-eyed optimists.

The uncertainties included the problems of finding a productive vein. For every successful mine there were many that brought little but hard labour and heartache. A potentially profitable vein of ore might run out sooner than expected. Even a good strike was no guarantee of a good living, for the price of lead on the open market was notoriously fickle. Indeed, the industry died in this country largely because of competition from mining operations overseas, rather than from any downturn in the demand for this most adaptable of metals.

We can look back on lead mining in the Dales to find two basic ways of working: individual miners operating independently, and companies which employed miners. Throughout the centuries we find this pattern repeated.

Mining on an industrial scale began in the seventeenth century, though most of the buildings to be seen today belong to the late 18th and 19th centuries. By the early 18th century we find lead mining progressing on rather more organised lines. Landowners whose land offered the prospect of wealth were naturally keen to exploit any lead that might be found, and negotiated the mineral rights with mining companies.

We find the Bathursts in Arkengarthdale, the Pomfrets-Denys family in Swaledale and the Duke of Devonshire on Grassington Moor, for example, leasing their mining fields to a succession of partnerships.

By and large the miners themselves were self-employed, enjoying, in theory at least, the freedom to work the hours they chose. Few men drew more than subsistence wages from their enterprises. Nevertheless, a few miners did make sufficiently profitable strikes to become shareholders in a mining company, and join the ranks of venture capitalists who put money – rather than their own labour – into the mines.

The most successful miners went on to become farmers and land-owners, enabling their families and descendants to enjoy a less precarious living away from the mines and the fickleness of the lead markets. These families were able to stay in the Dales at the end of the last century, when their less fortunate colleagues were forced to quit the mines and seek work elsewhere.

The miners valued their independence. They might go underground six days of the week, but they guarded their right to choose both their working hours and the time of starting their shifts. Indeed, one of the few strikes in the Dales mining fields occurred when a mining company tried to get the miners to start work each day at 7am.

The men typically worked six-hour shifts, significantly shorter than those in comparable industries. This pattern reflects both the hardship of the work, and the fact that many miners had a smallholding, and supplemented their variable incomes by keeping a cow, growing vegetables and perhaps even having a flock of sheep. They would thus be able to supplement a meagre diet of oatmeal porridge with home-grown vegetables, milk and perhaps a flitch of bacon. Salt beef and mutton might appear on the table to brighten a winter's evening; otherwise meat would have made but rare appearances. No doubt some miners would have taken to poaching – thereby adding a rabbit or hare to the cooking pot. The extra income derived from a smallholding, and the fresh air, were equally welcomed.

Miners were both adaptable and independent, and given to reading and nonconformist faith. A walk of five miles to work, and five miles home again, would have been unexceptional. It was common for men to knit as they walked. Other men would lodge (permanently – or during the working weeks) in a nearby mine shop.

Miners

Many miners supplemented their mining incomes by cutting peat for the smelt mills, breaking roadstone, building dry-stone walls, acting as guides for hunting parties and, at harvest time, making hay.

The miners' lot improved significantly when more ethical mining companies (such as the Quaker London Lead Company) brought venture capital into the Dales mining fields. The law, too, recognised the need to safeguard the rights of the miners, though legislation could generally be summed up as 'too little, too late'.

The business of lead mining was conducted in many different ways, though the terms of engagement not surprisingly tended to favour mining companies rather than individual workers. The miners of the Yorkshire Dales were not members of any union. Perhaps misguidedly they valued their independence too much. On the one hand they worked without a direct overseer (though there might be a mining agent or manager), and chose their own hours. On the other hand they were susceptible to the fluctuations of the lead market and enjoyed little financial security.

There's space here to offer merely a thumb-nail sketch of the possible working relationships that bound together landowners, mining companies, agents and the miners in a search for mineral wealth in some of the country's most isolated valleys.

Always a high-risk business, lead mining required venture capital. Money had to be ploughed – for months, perhaps even years – into driving levels, sinking shafts, constructing the smelt mills and other buildings. All this was before a single waggon of ore could be extracted or a single pig of lead sold on the open market.

Most miners of the 18th and 19th centuries worked to what was known as the bargain system. A partnership of miners would negotiate with a mine owner (or, more likely, his agent) to work a particular area. This bargain allowed the miners to extract ore for a specified length of time, and be paid according to a pre-determined calculation. This might be based per bing (a unit of weight equivalent to about 8 cwts of unsmelted bouse) or per 'pig' of smelted lead. At the end of the allotted time (a period of one to three months was common) the 'bargain' would be renegotiated afresh.

Lead Mining in the Yorkshire Dales

J Backhouse

At times when there was a glut of lead on the market, miners would be offered a lower price for their lead. Here a miner mans the hotching tub at Faggergill Mine in Arkengarthdale, circa 1910.

These short-term contracts allowed mine agents to change the terms (at the end of a bargain) if, for example, a vein was proving particularly profitable. At times when there was a glut of lead on the market, or a vein offered easy pickings, the miners would be offered a lower price for their lead.

Other criteria were taken into account when calculating the bargains. These included the quality of the ore being brought to the surface, the distance the ore had to be transported – first to the dressing floor and then on to the smelt mill. If the miners had to cut through unproductive grounds before they could bring out ore, then wages might be paid for this work.

Nevertheless, the bargain system tilted the balance in favour of the mine owners. If a rich vein was being mined, the miners would receive a lower price per bing than if they were working on a poor vein. The best the miners could hope for was to negotiate a rate for a vein that seemed to offer poor rewards, and then be lucky enough to strike a rich one. They might make a good profit on that bargain, and have every incentive to work longer hours, but the prices received for the next bargain they struck would be lowered accordingly.

Miners were naturally disinclined to cut through unproductive areas, because it would curtail their earnings. So some bargains would stipulate that the miners had to drive new levels, carry out maintenance work and do other essential jobs. These stipulations helped to ensure the long-term viability of a mine. It hardly needs saying that the bargain system was prone to shady dealing by all concerned: miners, owners and agents. Miners, for example, might be discreet about a particularly rich find of lead, in order to get a preferential deal when the bargain was renegotiated.

Lord Pomfret vented his frustrations, in 1773, about the problems of employing a local mining agent: "The only way to have a just account and to make a full profit of the Estates in Swaledale is not to employ anyone as a steward who is a Yorkshireman, and particularly of that neighborhood."

Leases might also stipulate that the miners would carry on working the veins right up to the end of the lease. Otherwise miners might be tempted, during the last few weeks of the lease, to bring out only that ore which was most easily won – thus jeopardising the mine's long-term future. Men other than miners – such as those working on the dressing floors and in the smelt mills – were usually paid in simpler fashion, by the shift.

Lead mining was never a well-paid occupation. In 1832, when a depression hit the country at large, the average wage for comparative work had dropped from 14s to just half that amount. Lead miners' wages might be, the Poor Law Commission heard, "£1 a week, at other times he may get only 3s a week, and sometimes nothing at all."

The peculiarities of the bargain system meant that miners might go for long periods between payments, during which time they might be running up debts with mining companies, the mine shop or perhaps local shopkeepers. Then, when pay day finally arrived, it might prove hard to resist the temptation to head for the ale house for a protracted celebration.

The men needed a modicum of financial security, and the mine owners needed a settled workforce. The solution, for both parties, lay in averaging out the miners' earnings, and providing the men with regular income. Some miners felt this took away some of their independence; others were glad to know exactly how much money they'd have in their hands on pay day. Monthly wages made it easier to budget and stay out of debt.

At the height of the industry in the Yorkshire Dales, during the middle years of the last century, nearly half the male workforce would have worked in the lead mines and smelt mills. The percentage climbed even higher in those areas, such as Swaledale, where mining was particularly prevalent. By the time Queen Victoria was being laid to rest, the industry was in terminal decline.

In 1851 the population of Grassington was 1,138, according to the census of that year; forty years later it was down to 480. Arkengarthdale could boast a population of 1,283 in 1851; the numbers have dwindled ever since. Melbecks, an area that included a number of mining fields in Swaledale, had 1,661 inhabitants in 1851; today there are only about 300.

This scale of depopulation is reflected throughout the mining fields of the Yorkshire Dales. Between the censuses of 1891 and 1971, the population of Swaledale was halved: a startling statistic.

Conditions

Despite the dangers of their work lead miners did not have the problems of potentially explosive gases that coal miners had to face. If a lead miner could not look forward to a long retirement, then much the same could be said for those in many other trades. Figures from Grassington district in 1860 show that lead miners lived to an average age of 45, whereas the average for the non-mining population was 55.

One problem associated with lead mining was known as miners' consumption. Rock dust, when inhaled, was responsible for the lung infections that brought many premature deaths. Health hazards were greatest in areas where sandstone was found, such as Swaledale. Here the miners could, in 1860, expect to live only to 46, compared with 60 for non-miners. In the mining fields of Greenhow Hill, where the workings were mostly found in limestone, miners lived significantly longer.

Poor ventilation was always a problem in the mines. A level driven into the hillside did not allow air to circulate freely; some kind of ventilation system was always needed. If dangerous gases were seldom found, oxygen, too, was often in such short supply that the miners' candles would go out.

A good supply of air was vital, and those mining companies that took a long-term view of their activities ensured that air pumps, ventilation shafts and cross-cuts were installed.

The problems of poor ventilation were multiplied by the nature of the miners' work. Picks and shovels raised dust; gunpowder blasts filled the air with fumes. Men working on piece-rate could seldom afford to wait until the fumes had fully cleared before getting back to work. By the time they were in their thirties many miners would be in poor health: broken-winded from breathing stale air, rock-dust and explosives.

The working conditions were no better in the smelt mills. The smelting process generated sulphur dioxide gas, together with a

Lead Mining in the Yorkshire Dales

certain amount of lead in the form of vapour. The dangers of these gases were well known by the early years of the 19th century, and a number of safety measures were gradually introduced.

Long flues, sometimes as much as a mile in length, carried fumes far from the mill, away from vegetation and the lungs of smelters and grazing animals. Many older mills, with integral chimneys, were improved by the later addition of flues. It is ironic that men were known to have lost their lives while working in these flues, scraping lead deposits off the walls. The presence of arsenic made this work even more hazardous.

Accidents were more usually associated with the fabric of the mines, with roof-falls being an ever-present possibility. When levels had to be reinforced, this was usually done with stone; structural problems were more likely when wood was used. Shafts, too, were often fitted with wooden rungs built into the sides. When these rungs rotted and failed, a potentially fatal fall could result. Yet accounts reveal that more Swaledale miners were drowned trying to cross the River Swale in flood than were killed in mining accidents.

Childhood didn't last long in the lead mining areas of the Yorkshire Dales. Boys typically left school at ten years of age to work at the mines, so literacy could not be taken for granted. With neither the strength nor the experience to toil at the ore-faces with pick or shovel, they took on a number of less demanding – though boringly repetitive – tasks.

One job was to blow air into poorly ventilated areas of the mine, using a machine known as a 'windy king'. Some boys would load hoppers with ore mined at the face, and drag them through the levels and out onto the dressing floor. Here, in the open air, other children would be wielding buckers: hammers for crushing the ore. Children would operate the hotching tubs and buddles. They habitually worked full shifts, with little or no protection from the cold and rain.

Women, too, often worked on the dressing floors – crushing and buddling the bouse to make it fine and pure enough for smelting. The women often worked longer hours on the dressing floors than their menfolk did down the mines. On their way to work the women

Conditions

Beamish Museum Collection

Miners at the Grassington field would have had a long walk to and from their work. Pictured are supports for the winding rope to Moss Shaft on Grassington Moor in Wharfedale.

habitually knitted; the sale of their knitted garments did much to supplement the family's meagre income. The men, too, would pick up their needles whenever they had a few minutes to spare.

With many of the mines sited in isolated valleys, the miners often worked a good distance from their homes. A walk of three miles to work would not be uncommon, with the prospect of walking the same distance at the end of the shift: weary, hungry and perhaps chilled to the bone.

Lead Mining in the Yorkshire Dales

Home might be an isolated dwelling or a simple house in one of the many villages – such as Reeth, Gunnerside and Grassington – near the mining fields. Such villages expanded rapidly while the mining was profitable, often by inbuilding: new buildings would be 'shoehorned' in wherever there was room – which was often in the yards and gardens of existing properties.

You can still see some of the miners' lonely farmsteads beneath the moor tops, hemmed in by 'intakes': small walled fields taken in from the fells to form a smallholding. Many of these houses are at a height unsuitable for growing anything other than hay; no-one could have eked out a living at such altitudes by farming alone. Nevertheless, the miners were always keen to acquire a little land.

While house rents tended to be low (the mining companies being keen to maintain a pool of miners in the vicinity), land was comparatively expensive. High land rents were partly due to the competition between miners to lease fields whenever they became available.

The miners' independent nature, and their relatively short working hours, enabled them to carry on this dual economy of mining and farming. At hay-time, for example, the miners might take a few days off from mining to bring in the hay, or even to work for neighbouring farmers. As an indication of how hard the work was in the mines, the men regarded a few days of farming as a holiday.

From the late 18th century to the middle of the 19th, much common land was divided up and enclosed. It is to this period that the majority of the dry stone field-walls belong. Walling was another trade by which some of the miners would supplement their incomes.

The isolation of many of the mining fields meant that some miners had little option but to live there during the week, returning home only at weekends. The London Lead Company, for example, operating further north in Weardale, provided basic accommodation, known as mine shops, for those miners who needed lodgings during the week. These buildings were sited as close to the mines as possible. The mine shop at Killhope (now carefully restored) was only a few yards from the Park Head Level.

An example of lead mining remains above Storthwaite Farm in lonely Arkengarthdale. Hushes are visible on the hillside near Slei Gill.

The hushes in the vicinity of Slei Gill near Langthwaite make an impressi

ht. Mining debris and spoil heaps add to the sense of lunar desolation.

Crackpot Hall (above) near Keld boasts one of the finest views in the Dales. Pictured below is a former bell pit on Grassington Moor.

Conditions

Other mining companies built lodging shops at their mines. Here, between shifts, the men could dry their clothes, cook basic meals, and warm themselves by the fire. They would sleep in bunks, usually two or more to a bed. The shift system operating at many of the mines ensured that the beds were seldom allowed to go cold: as men were getting out of bed to face another shift down the mine, others would be wearily crawling under the pile of filthy blankets.

To judge from contemporary accounts, lodging shops were dirty, foul-smelling and grossly overcrowded. Imagine a rack of wet, dirty clothes hung in front of a fire, food cooking in rancid fat, unwashed men in the closest of proximity, and you have a scene as squalid as you would have found in the meanest of city slums.

A mine inspector wrote, in 1842: "I should think it no hardship to have to remain twenty-four hours in a mine, but I should be terrified of being ordered to be shut up a quarter of an hour in the bedroom of a lodging shop."

The isolation of the settlements in the Yorkshire Dales produced a hardy, self-reliant population, which gravitated with a passion towards nonconformist religions. In the 17th century Swaledale offered a willing ear to the preaching of George Fox, the founder of Quakerism. Later the London Lead Company combined business acumen with Quaker sensibilities to bring more enlightened attitudes to the industry.

In 1761 a small group of Methodists gathered in Low Row, Swaledale, to hear John Wesley preach. He was later to recall this gathering as "one of the most lively which I have met with ..." The uncompromising nature of Methodism appealed to the miners' independence of spirit, and chapels were built – often through public subscription – in many of the Dales' villages. Travelling preachers were dispatched to the remotest hamlets.

The Methodist flock split in 1812, with the Primitive Methodists breaking away from the Wesleyans. The 'Prims' held impassioned open-air meetings, of a kind that would be familiar to those who attend the revivalist rallies of today.

Lonely Greenhow Hill, a stronghold of Methodism, also witnessed a rebirth of Congregationalism, with the preachers' visits being paid for out of the lead miners' wages.

These nonconformist faiths persuaded many miners and their families away from the established church. Indeed, the decline of Methodism in the northern Dales can be traced directly to the decline in the industry, with so many miners and their families leaving for pastures new.

The lead miners quarried much of the stone for these chapels, and often undertook the building work. Their spiritual needs having found a focus, they next turned their attentions to education. Libraries and literary institutes flourished, providing places to meet, read and listen to improving lectures.

When the Conformity laws outlawed some of the nonconformist ministers, outdoor services were conducted (or so the story goes) at Swinnergill Kirk, a small cave close to the the lead smelting mill in Swinnergill, between Muker and Keld. Methodists, Primitive Methodists, Congregationalists and Baptists all contributed much to chapel life in the Yorkshire Dales.

The lead miners had little security of income. For example, a depression from 1829 to 1833 forced many small mines to close. Those mining companies that survived only did so by cutting the mens' wages, and by having sufficient capital to ride out the slump.

The larger mining concerns were better able to withstand these depressions. Companies with venture capital could afford to take a longer-term view and, when times were hard, keep men employed on tasks which, though necessary, were not likely to bring immediate profits. Miners would be set to building roads, extending levels and doing maintenance work. Experience told these companies that prices would rise again, and those that survivived the slump between 1829 to 1833 were able to take advantage of the boom times during the 1840s and 1850s.

A good yield of lead was no guarantee of good wages; the hitting of a rich vein might coincide with a period of poor prices or low demand. There were times when it wasn't considered worthwhile to bring ore out of even the most productive mines. Cruelly, the bargain

Conditions

system – in which mining partnerships agreed terms with companies for mining lead for a given period – didn't always reward hard work or good fortune.

At times when ore was easily won, and prices high, the miners were keen to work. During one of the periodic slumps in the industry, the men would want to continue working simply because there was no other work to be had. Thus it was that the lead miners of the Yorkshire Dales never became unionised. Strikes did occur from time to time, but they were generally in response to one single circumstance or conflict, and disputes did not spread, in any organised way, from mine to mine.

Though working conditions were harsh, the 19th century saw a more enlightened outlook by mining companies. Some of the companies' welfare schemes stemmed from self-interest, as it was to their benefit to be able to call upon a settled, fit and solvent workforce. The Poor Law of 1834 gave provision for small sums to be distributed among the needy. Those who hit hard times could look forward only to the ultimate disgrace: old age in the workhouse.

Dr John Bathurst, whose successors created the CB Company, took a paternalistic view of his miners and tenants in Arkengarthdale. He founded and funded a free school for the children of the dale, and gave financial provision for poor widows – or at least those who were regular church attenders.

The Yorkshire Dales were isolated, and most people lived and died in the same village where they were born. So it is not surprising that the same surnames – Metcalf and Fawcett, for example – crop up again and again. With so many men sharing the same surname, and often the Christian name, too, nicknames were used.

The pubs and beer houses provided warmth, companionship and a good way for the miners to burn a hole in their wages. Once Methodism took hold, however, the number of pubs declined, as the men spent fewer hours at the bar, and instead spent more time trying to better themselves, both spiritually and educationally, at chapel and institute. Then men started clubs, brass bands, and so on.

With few opportunities to put meat on the table in any other way, the miners might indulge in a little poaching. In an attempt, perhaps, to forestall such illicit activities, miners were often employed as beaters for local grouse shoots. Spending so much time in the gloom, the miners were commonly thought to be blessed with particularly keen eyesight.

Place Names

The lead mining districts of the Yorkshire Dales boast place-names that range from the mellifluous to the frankly bizarre. Langthwaite in Arkengarthdale has a fine ring to it; Booze and Crackpot Hall can hardly fail to raise a smile, though the derivation of their names is at best ambiguous.

Clues to the presence of lead mining fields can be gleaned from consulting both old and current maps. The words 'bail', 'bale', 'baal' and 'bole' usually indicate a windswept, open-air site where lead was once smelted. 'Grooves' and 'groves' (both common) give clues to the presence of old mines and bell pits.

The road between the Arkengarthdale mines and the long-demolished smelt mill at Clints was called Oregate. The name still appears on maps – as does Jagger Lane, the name of an old packhorse track along which smelted ore was carried to the ports of Stockton and Yarm.

Here are likely derivations of some of the places associated with lead mining in the Yorshire Dales:

Appletreewick: The dairy farm by the apple tree.

Arkengarthdale: The dale of Arkil's enclosure.

Booze: 'The house by the bend' or possibly from 'bouse', the miners' term for unsmelted ore.

Clint: Rocky cliff.

Cogden: Woodcock valley.

Crackpot Hall: 'A pothole where crows live'.

Faggergill: Ravine in a sheep enclosure.

Dr J O Myers

Langthwaite means 'Long Clearing'. This is the Octagon Mill at Langthwaite, Arkengarthdale, in 1946.

Fremington: Frema's farm.

Grassington: Grazing farm.

Grinton: Green enclosure.

Gunnerside: Gunnar's summer pasture.

Hebden: Bramble valley.

Hurst: Wooded hill.

Place Names

Keld: A spring.

Kettlewell: The bubbling spring.

Langthwaite: Long clearing.

Marrick: Horse ridge.

Muker: Small field.

Old Gang: The old road.

Redmire: Reed pool.

Reeth: The stream.

Glossary

The lead miners had a rich vocabulary to describe the processes and equipment associated with their livelihood. Here is a selection of words that were familiar in the Yorkshire Dales:

Adit: Underground tunnel, driven into a hillside, for giving access to mine workings or for draining water.

Bail hill: Crude ore-smelting hearth, constructed from stones against a hillside, using the strength of the prevailing wind to bring the fire up to smelting temperature. (Also 'bell bank', 'bale', 'baill', 'baal' and 'bole'.)

Bargain: A short-term contract agreed between teams of miners, or between miners and mine agent, to work a particular mine, or extract a particular amount of ore.

Bell pit: A name often given to what might more properly be called a shallow shaft. An early method of digging down into a lead-bearing vein, and widening the shaft as far as could be safely dug.

Bing: A measurement of weight, applied to excavated material: usually about 8 cwt (400 kg).

Bingstead: A building or container used for storing lead ore, prior to being smelted.

Bouse: Lead-bearing ore, as brought out of a mine, before it is dressed or smelted.

Bouseteam: Building or container for storing bouse (mined ore before it is dressed).

Glossary

Buddle: A shallow pit in which running water is used to separate lead-ore from other materials.

Bucker: Broad-headed hammer for breaking up ore into a size suitable for smelting.

Chats: Stones with small amounts of lead ore in them, needing to be crushed on the dressing floor.

Chopwood: coppiced wood which, when dried out, was used as a fuel in the smelt mills.

Concentrate: Dressed ore, ready for smelting.

Condenser: A widened area of a flue, often filled with brushwood, for the purpose of condensing the lead content from the fumes going up the flue. The brushwood could then be burned to recover the lead oxide.

Cross cut: Level or tunnel driven through a dead (unproductive) area, to link two mining levels.

Cupola furnace: Another name for a reverberatory furnace.

Dead ground: Unproductive area of a mine.

Deads: Waste material discarded during any of the mining processes.

Dead men: Miners working on jobs that didn't produce ore, such as cutting levels, walling, etc.

Dressing floor: Flat area where ore was broken up and separated into galena for smelting, and waste material for discarding.

Lead Mining in the Yorkshire Dales

Elling hearth: Simple structures sited in woodland, in which chopwood could be dried prior to being taken as fuel to the smelt mills.

Engine shaft: A shaft equipped with an engine for pumping or hoisting.

Face: The end of a mine tunnel where ore was mined.

Fathom: A measurement of length used by miners, about 6 feet.

Feathers: Mining tools (see Plug).

Flue: A long 'chimney' built uphill from a smelt mill, and usually along the ground, which served the twin purposes of taking poisonous fumes away from the mill and creating a strong draught for the furnace.

Fuse: Slow-burning device, usually filled with gunpowder, to enable miners to light their explosives and get to a safe position before the explosion.

Galena: Lead sulphide.

Galloway: A pack pony.

Galloway level: Mine level built tall enough to allow ponies to pull waggons along a railway.

Gangue: Waste material, made up of minerals other than lead ore.

Gin: A horse-powered winding device, for drawing ore up vertical shafts.

Glossary

Groove: A mine (often of an open-cast type); a groover is a miner.

Horse-gin: A winding shaft for drawing mined materials to the surface, powered by a horse walking around a winding gear. This method superceded the jack-roller.

Horse-level: A level or tunnel tall enough to accommodate horses, for pulling the waggons.

Horse-whim: A winding shaft for drawing mined materials to the surface, powered by a horse walking around a winding-gear.

Hotching: A method of separating ore from dead material, by repeatedly sieving up and down in a hotching tub.

Hush: A vein worked by damming up water and letting it rush down, thus uncovering new areas of vein.

Hush gutter: Trench dug downhill from a dammed-up head of water to channel the torrent of water, during hushing, towards the lead-bearing vein beneath.

Jack-roller: Hand-operated winch for drawing mined material up a shaft.

Jumper: Hand-held drill for making holes in rock.

Kibble: Bucket used to wind mined material up a vertical shaft.

Launder: Channel for conveying water to a waterwheel.

Leat: Water channel.

Level: Horizontal tunnel in a mine.

Lode: Ore-bearing vein.

Lead Mining in the Yorkshire Dales

Meer: A variable unit of measurement (usually about 30 metres, at least in the Yorkshire Dales' mining fields), where the ground leased by different mining partnerships had to be identified. Meer stones (a few still survive) were inscribed with the names – or often just the initials – of the mining partnership concerned.

Mine agent: The General Manager of a mine.

Needle: Narrow tool used to make a hole in mining explosives, to enable a fuse to be fitted. Early needles, made of iron or steel, created sparks which sometimes ignited the explosive prematurely – with tragic results. With an eye to safety, an Act of Parliament was passed, insisting that needles be made of copper.

Old man: A general term to describe miners of earlier times – the spirit of mining past. Often used to indicate older, unrecorded workings found when driving new levels.

Peat house: A building made for storing peat, one of the fuels commonly used in the smelting process.

Pig: An ingot of smelted lead.

Plug: Plug and feathers were the usual method of breaking up rock in the mine, before the introduction of gunpowder. The plug was an iron wedge, which was driven into the rock between two flat pieces of iron, known as feathers. In this way, cracks could be opened up to split the rockface apart.

Portal: The entrance to a mining level.

Pricker: Tool to make a hole in explosives, in order to insert a fuse (see Needle).

The crushing roller and waterwheel at Old Providence Mine, Kettlewell, in Wharfedale. The crusher reduced lead into a size suitable for smelting.

Dr A Raistrick

Reverberatory furnace: A type of furnace, introduced about 1700, which was designed for continuous running and smelting large quantities of lead ore. The lead ore did not come into contact with the fire, but the heat was reflected onto the concentrate.

Roasting hearth: Furnace for heating ore before smelting, to remove some of the sulphur content.

Lead Mining in the Yorkshire Dales

Roller crusher: Machine for crushing bouse into fragments of a size suitable for smelting. Rock was crushed between heavy rollers, as in a giant mangle.

Slag: Waste produced by the smelting process.

Slag hearth: Furnace for resmelting slag, to extract some of the remaining concentration of lead.

Slimes: Finely ground material remaining at the end of the crushing and buddling processes. It could be collected in a slime pit, and then rebuddled to extract ore.

Smelting: The conversion of lead mineral to metal by raising to a high temperature in a furnace.

Smitham(s) (or smiddums): Fine aggregate of ore, after being crushed on the dressing floor.

Spoil: Waste material left over from the separation processes on the dressing floor; it was generally tipped to form spoil-heaps.

Stope: A worked-out portion of a vein.

Stemples: Wooden beams laid across a shaft, for climbing, or to give support to a level.

Sump: Shaft sunk below the water-table, so that the water could be pumped out of a mine.

Sumpter pot: A metal container into which molten ore would collect during the smelting process. Ore would be ladled out of the sumpter pot and into moulds, to create lead ingots.

Turnrail: A simple 'points' system used to switch a waggon from one track to another, by means of one movable rail.

Vein: A deposit of lead ore in the ground, usually in the form of a vertical ribbon.

Waggon: Wheeled container, run along rails through a level, to transport ore and deads out of the mine, and tools and materials to the vein being worked.

Whim: Method of winding containers up and down a shaft; the motive power might be a horse, steam, or water.

Windy king: Mechanical device for ventilating a mine; operating it was typically a job for a boy.

Section Two

The Walks – Introduction

There are hundreds of mining sites in the Yorkshire Dales, but only a few repay the effort required to visit them. Minor sites can be found, by chance, in any of the northern Dales, so these six walks concentrate on those major sites that are both easily accessible and rich in mining remains. All are bracing walks in their own right; those with no interest in mining history will find much else to delight the eye.

The walks vary in length, from the shortest of strolls to more than six miles (10km), and all use paths that are both clearly discernible 'on the ground' and recognised as rights-of-way on Ordnance Survey maps. The mining fields are criss-crossed with permissive paths and other routes which, while regularly used by walkers, are not designated as rights-of-way.

Walkers wanting to learn more about the lead mines and the smelt mills should consider joining one of the guided walks organised by the National Park. A list of walks can be found in the National Park's annual publication, *The Visitor*. Knowledgeable guides can interpret the mining remains and help to bring the industry to life.

While the maps in this book are sufficient for negotiating the walks, you should also carry the appropriate Ordnance Survey map. My routes are merely suggestions; once you have a map you will be able to vary your route if the spirit takes you.

There are, for example, dozens of paths you could take across the far-flung mining fields of Grassington Moor, and an OS map will help you to interpret what you will see. More importantly, if you do

Lead mining enthusiasts enjoying a guided walk at Grinton Mine.

Gunnerside Gill is splendid walking country. Today, it is a peaceful sp

ce it was a hive of lead mining activity, as the many remains indicate.

Walkers stroll amid lead mining's legacy in Gunnerside Gill (above). The Powder House near Langthwaite (below) is a marvellous relic.

Walks Introduction

manage to get lost, you will need an OS map to 'read' the landmarks and rejoin the route.

One feature of lead mines is the intricate network of paths created for the transportation of galena and fuel to the smelt mills, and pigs of smelted lead towards trading centres such as Pateley Bridge, Richmond and Yarm. If you half close your eyes you can almost see the trains of 'Galloways', packponies with their pannier bags filled with lead ore or coal, and hear the tinkling of their bells. These same tracks provide easy walking today, without any need for rock-scrambling.

It is a hundred years since most of these mining areas rang with noise, and much has changed in the intervening years. Most buildings surplus to requirements have not been maintained. Some are still standing to substantially their full height, making it easy to see how they would have looked at the height of the industry. Others, alas, are now little more than heaps of rubble. Some, such as the monumental Octagon Mill at Langthwaite, were summarily demolished and live on only in old photographs. So each walk has notes to give plenty of information.

These are historic sites; please treat them with care, by not climbing on walls, removing stones or otherwise defacing old mining buildings. Their importance is now being recognised, and some sites (such as the smelt mills at Old Gang and Grinton) are being consolidated, in order to avoid further deterioration.

Lastly, another reminder to think twice before venturing underground. The mines are labyrinthine, intrinsically unstable and few of the shafts and levels have seen any maintenance work since the miners put down their picks and shovels for the last time a century ago. You have been warned ...

Walk One

Gunnerside Gill

The village of Gunnerside comprises a compact huddle of houses lying either side of Gunnerside Beck. At one time the beck formed the boundary between two settlements, called Gunnerside and, to the east, Lodge Green. Now the name Gunnerside applies to the whole community.

The village is an evocative reminder of the Norse settlers who came to the remoter dales. Gunnerside means *Gunnar's Saetr*: that is, summer pasture. The economy relied to a large extent on the lead mines of Gunnerside Gill, and its population figures chart the industry's fluctuating fortunes. During the most productive years the population of Gunnerside rose to about 700, about three times the number today.

Mines and Mills

The principal mining fields of Gunnerside Gill exploit the same, east-west orientated veins as the mines of Beldi Hill, Swinner Gill and Hard Level – all visited in other walks. You can connect the main veins on an Ordnance Survey map, simply by drawing a straight line from the villages of Keld in Swaledale to Langthwaite in Arkengarthdale. If you trace a finger along this line, you will notice large areas of hushes, mining waste and shafts. This mining field was one of the most productive in the Pennines, and nowhere was it worked more extensively than in Gunnerside Gill.

The valley runs north-south, cutting across these veins. The steep sides of the valley made hushing the ideal way of finding and exploiting lead-bearing veins. How successful this method was can be gauged from the size of the hushes: huge, bare, rocky, wholly man-made side-valleys descending right down to Gunnerside Beck.

Gunnerside Gill Walk

To reach the veins from lower levels than was possible by hushing, mining levels were driven into the valley sides, and the entrances to a number of them can be seen on this walk.

The Sir Francis mine was owned by Sir George Denys, who held the mineral rights to a number of mining fields in Swaledale. The mine was named after his son. Sir George started driving the horse level in 1864. A long drive was needed to reach productive ground, but early progress was hampered by the hardness of the rock. The work speeded up only when he introduced new rock-drills, operated by compressed air. The compressor was powered by a gigantic waterwheel, with a diameter of 12m. The ruined wheel-pit can still be seen, but the wheel itself is long gone. The wheel-pit and receiver can be found just a few feet above the entrance to the Sir Francis Level, on the west bank of Gunnerside Gill.

Dynamite, used after 1873, also helped to speed up the driving of the level. Four years later the productive Friarfold vein was broached. The level served another useful purpose, draining water from a number of mines further up Gunnerside Gill.

The Sir Francis Level opened up a number of veins, giving such good quantities of ore that two dressing floors were built – on either side of the beck – to crush and prepare the ore for smelting. One belonged to the Old Gang Company, the other to the A D Company. Originally these dressing floors were connected by a wooden bridge, over which waggons of ore could be pulled on rails. The bridge has not survived, though the remains of its stone foundations can be seen on both banks. To power the waterwheel, water from the beck was diverted along aqueducts, which were raised up on pillars. These, too, are gone, leaving just the waterwheel pits.

Dressed ore from the Old Gang operation was taken to the Old Gang Smelt Mill in the next valley to the east (see walk 3). Instead of the ore being carried overland, it was taken up Gunnerside Gill to the Bunton Level, and transported underground into the Old Gang workings. Going through the hill into Hard Level Gill was reckoned to be a cheaper option than going over the top. The A D Company smelted their bouse at Surrender Mill, further down Hard Level Gill.

Lead Mining in the Yorkshire Dales

The price of lead was subject to fluctuations; at times it was hardly worthwhile bringing ore out of even the most productive mines. In 1882 a price slump almost closed the mine; by the time mining was resumed the hydraulic engine was found to be badly damaged by water. The Sir Francis mine was never worked again.

Further up Gunnerside Gill is a massive mining field, made up of huge hushes that scar the valley sides, plus some fascinating remains. What is most striking, however, is the sheer scale of the operation, with the landscape ravaged by hushes and spoil heaps for hundreds of yards in whatever direction you care to look. The scene is breathtaking.

The Lownathwaite mines tunnel west, and meet up with the Swinner Gill mine field (see walk 2). A little further up, and also on the west side of the beck, are Sun and North hushes. They face, across the beck, a trio of hushes: Gorton, Friarfold and Bunton. Most of the levels were driven after hushing had uncovered lead-bearing veins as far down as was practicable. Two levels – Bunton and Sir George – were driven into the valley side from the base of Bunton hush.

The entrance to Bunton Level can be found inside the ruins of a small building; nearby are the mining office, bouseteams and waterwheel pit. Across the beck are other buildings and the arched entrances to Dolly, Woodward and Priscilla levels. All these levels linked into the extensive Friarfold vein.

Towards the top of Gunnerside Gill, on a flat triangle of land where Blind Gill meets Gunnerside Gill, is Blakethwaite mill. This compact site has the ruined smelt mill, peat house and, a little way up Blind Gill, a mining level. Note how the flue from the smelt mill's furnaces was ingeniously built up the rocky cliff at the back, ending in a ruined chimney stack.

Once Lownathwaite mill had been abandoned in 1827, all ore from the mining fields at the head of Gunnerside Gill was smelted here at Blakethwaite mill. It was operated until 1878.

Investigations further north reveal the remains of a dressing floor, almost at beck level, then, finally, Blakethwaite Dams, which ensured a good head of water throughout the year for turning the waterwheels.

Gunnerside Gill Walk

The Walk

Park: Gunnerside (SD 951 982). Map: OS Outdoor Leisure 30 (Yorkshire Dales, Northern & Central). Length: 6 miles (10km). Grading: Moderate.

Park in Gunnerside and walk to the little bridge in the centre of the village, that spans Gunnerside Beck. Take a track on the eastern side up the beck, that begins opposite the King's Arms pub. Follow the beck upstream; after 100 metres the track ends at a white gate. Here take stone steps to the right, then a walled path. Once through a little gate, bear left to emerge into open fields. Your path ahead is clear, following the course of Gunnerside Beck.

Just before you enter a wood, you will see the first tangible sign of mining activity: a small spoil heap and arched entrance to a mine level, now blocked up. Go through a gate and follow a well-defined path, up and down, in and out of woodland. The path descends to the beck as the valley broadens out. Cross a side beck on a tiny plank bridge. Go through two gap stiles, close together, and follow a wall. Once through two little gates, you reach the beck once again, and the walk's first major evidence of lead ore processing.

The path takes you straight to the first of two ore-dressing floors on the Sir Francis mining complex. The floor is raised, and it was here that the ore would be crushed, sorted and buddled to achieve a more concentrated lead content for smelting. That much of the crushing became mechanised is indicated by the presence of a waterwheel pit.

Above the dressing floor, and a few yards upstream, are the bouseteams, where the mining partnerships would store their ore prior to crushing. These are of the usual shape, with the back of the bays rounded off. There are ten bouseteams, indicating how busy the Sir Francis Mine must have been. A rail-track at the back of the bouseteams allowed ore to be tipped directly into the bays from above. A tally hut also remains.

Continue along the riverside path, following the yellow

waymarking arrows. A little detour to the right is necessary, before you get back to the beck again. This was once another rail track, and the marks left by the sleepers can still be discerned in places.

Across the water is another dressing floor, and a building that served as the mine office. Here too is the entrance to the Sir Francis Level, tall enough for horses, and the cast-iron air receiver that helped to power the rock-boring drills. It took a dozen horses to haul this massive compressor to this isolated spot. There used to be a bridge over Gunnerside Beck at this point; it has long since disappeared, leaving just traces of the stone-built foundation piers.

Your path is uphill at this point, away from the beck and through a gap stile in a wall. The path climbs gradually, as the valley becomes steeper-sided. Keep a wall to your left; soon the path levels out to give easy, grassy walking towards the principal mining area of Gunnerside Gill. Across the valley looms Botcher Gill – more of a ravine than a side valley, and punctuated by little waterfalls.

The next landmark on the opposite side of Gunnerside Gill is the Dolly Mine, comprising the entrance to a level, an old wheel-pit, bouseteams and the remains of a dressing floor. Beneath these high-level workings, the spoil heaps fall away in rocky screes, down to the beck below.

Soon the Bunton Mine complex comes into view, on 'your' side of the valley. A scene of stunning devastation unfolds that makes the next mile an almost totally man-made landscape of hushes, spoil-heaps and screes. As you reach the Bunton workings the waterwheel pit is a prominent feature. Notice the arched aperture on the lower end; this was for the outflow of water. Close by is a line of bouseteams; there appear to be seventeen or eighteen bays. Bunton was, for many years, the most productive lead mining site in the Dales.

The next feature of note is the arched entrance to Bunton Level, with the great Bunton Hush rising up behind it. The mill buildings stand on a level area that was made from an extensive spoil heap. The buildings comprised the mine office, stables and a blacksmith's shop.

Across the gill, and at a similar height, is the Lownathwaite Mine

Gunnerside Gill Walk

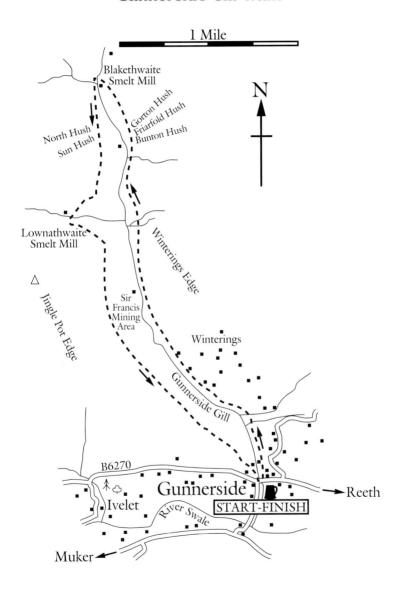

1 Mile

Blakethwaite
Smelt Mill

Gorton Hush
Friarfold Hush
Bunton Hush

North Hush
Sun Hush

N

Lownathwaite
Smelt Mill

Winterings Edge

△

Jingle Pot Edge

Sir
Francis
Mining
Area

Winterings

Gunnerside Gill

B6270

Gunnerside

Ivelet

START-FINISH

→ Reeth

River Swale

Muker ←

complex. The windows of a store building stare across the abyss and across the years. Once these remote sites rang with noise; now the silence is almost tangible.

Leave the Bunton Mine on a stony uphill path. To the right the Friarfold hush soon appears, matched, across the valley, by North and Sun hushes. This is the most heavily exploited area of Gunnerside Gill. At the base of Friarfold Hush is a meeting of paths. The easiest way to reach the smelt mill at Blakethwaite is to go left here, downhill.

Follow the path, noticing the entrance to Priscilla Mine on the far side of the beck. Just above the beck can be seen the remains of an old iron waggon. You approach Blakethwaite Mill accompanied by the noise of water tumbling over rocks; at this point Blind Beck meets Gunnerside Beck. The buildings are grouped in a way that seems to fit in with their rugged and isolated surroundings. The first building you come across is the peat store. One side of the building is a solid wall (apart from a couple of tiny windows), while the other side has four open arches facing the beck.

To reach the smelt mill you must cross the beck on a small bridge: a stonework base supports a single slab of stone. The mill building is much collapsed, making interpretation difficult. One wall, however, still stands to its full height, giving an indication of the building's original size.

The western portion of the building (left, if looking from the bridge) contained two ore hearths and a roasting hearth. The furnaces had sturdy stone hoods, built in the form of arches. These have collapsed, leaving only the cast iron pillars in place on which the arches were supported. The mill contained a waterwheel (7m in diameter). Water to turn the wheel came from three dams, further up the valley, and was conveyed to the wheel via a wooden launder. Behind the mill the flue (mostly collapsed) rises steeply uphill. To the right of the flue is a splendid example of a limekiln.

From the mill your return path is clear – following a well-defined path gradually climbing up the west flank of Gunnerside Gill. This is

Gunnerside Gill Walk

the route that would have been taken by trains of packhorses laden down with panniers of smelted lead. Cross the beck that runs down from Blind Gill, and begin the ascent. Once the track has levelled out, look across the valley to see the paths you took earlier, and the many other tracks that criss-cross the valley side.

The hushes of Gorton, Friarfold and Bunting look even more spectacular from a distance than they did from close quarters. Note the entrance to Gorton Mine beneath Gorton Hush. You cross North Hush by means of a stone parapet; soon the southern end of Gunnerside Gill – and the Sir Francis Mine workings – comes into view.

Follow the track as it becomes stonier, makes a hairpin turn to cross Botcher Gill and joins a more substantial track. Follow this track to the left, through a gate and past a little waterfall in Botcher Gill. You can lengthen your stride along this broad track that soon begins a gentle descent.

Across the valley the landscape changes from one of mining devastation to a more familiar one of field walls, sheepfolds, limekilns and barns. The walls create small fields of irregular shape; they are some of the oldest enclosures in the area. Winterings is a small collection of farm buildings; further toward Gunnerside the farms are grouped under the name of Potterings.

When the track makes a long right hand turn, strike off left, by a small cairn. Keep left (the track soon becomes more distinct) and head for the roofs of Gunnerside that soon begin to appear. The path gradually becomes clearer and leads you downhill, to enjoy birds'-eye views of Gunnerside. Go through a little wooden gate and back into the village.

Walk Two

Keld and Swinner Gill

This walk in Upper Swaledale is a splendid ramble, which includes a number of interesting sites associated with lead mining and smelting. There are also enough panoramic views to keep any companions happy who may not be interested in lead-mining.

The walk can be extended with a visit to the village of Muker, a pub lunch at the Miner's Arms and finished off in style with an exhilarating high-level walk back over Kisdon Hill. There are many footpaths linking Keld and Muker; all offer glorious views of Swaledale.

I wanted to include on this walk a visit to the Beldi Hill dressing floor, situated down by the River Swale. It is the best-preserved example of a dressing floor within the National Park, and provides a fascinating glimpse into the processes by which newly-mined galena was converted into a size and density that was ready for smelting. Much work has already been done to restore the dressing floor. It is, however, on private land and, at the time of writing, there is no longer any public access.

Mines and Mills

Quarrels between miners and mine owners could become quite acrimonious, and the Beldi Hill Mines were the subject of long, drawn-out litigation. The story is worth retelling, albeit briefly.

Crackpot Hall, a substantial house with as spectacular a view as

Keld and Swinner Gill Walk

any in the Yorkshire Dales, was built by Lord Wharton, whose family lived here for 200 years. In 1738 the property was bought by Thomas Smith, though the Wharton estate kept control of the mineral rights for some of the adjacent common land. Four years later a trio of brothers, John, Thomas and Ralph Parkes and one Leonard Hartley, leased the rights to mine at Beldi Hill from Smith. Parkes and Company drove Parkes Level on the western side of Swinner Gill. To the east of Swinner Gill other workings were being dug by miners working for Lord Pomfret, who had acquired the Wharton estate by marriage.

Once Parkes Level had been completed, Lord Pomfret asked to be able to use it, in order to gain access to some of his own workings. Parkes and Company agreed to this arrangement at first, but then found themselves digging through unproductive ground. They decided to abandon Parkes Level and a moorland stream was diverted into it. This flooded some of Lord Pomfret's workings as well, starting a quarrel between the two mining companies. Disputes over boundaries and mineral rights kept two teams of lawyers busy for years.

Both companies drove more levels, and built their own smelt mills. Lord Pomfret's was up Swinner Gill; the Parkes partnership built theirs lower down, at Beldi Hill, closer to where Swinner Gill Beck joins the River Swale. Both can be seen on this walk.

A further quarrel arose, with both Thomas Smith and Lord Pomfret believing that they owned the mineral rights to a productive area known as Hall Out Pasture, just above the Crackpot Hall. The dispute became ever more acrimonious, as Lord Pomfret took Smith to court in an attempt to prove his case.

Meanwhile, back at the Beldi Hill Mines, the miners, too, were at loggerheads. When Pomfret's men began to dig a new shaft, Parkes's men came in the night and filled it in. A fight broke out over the ownership of a batch of smelted lead, and Pomfret's men seized it. Fearing more skullduggery, Parkes's men transported 500 tons of ore from Beldi Hill Smelt Mill, in order to store it in a group of cow-byres. Unfortunately, the walls could not withstand this amount of ore, and one of the buildings collapsed. At one point Smith's and Pomfret's men were fist-fighting underground.

Mines were flooded, noses were bloodied, plans were thwarted. And, in the law courts of York, Lord Pomfret was losing his case. Three appeals to the House of Lords fell on deaf ears; the final verdict forced him to pay Thomas Smith the sum of £400 as compensation for damage to the mines. These protracted lawsuits drove Lord Pomfret deep into debt, and he was subsequently incarcerated in the Tower of London.

The Walk

Park: Keld (NY 893 012). Map: OS Outdoor Leisure 30 (Yorkshire Dales, Northern & Central). Length: 3.5 miles (5km). Grading: Moderate.

Park in Keld village, taking care not to block any access for residents. Your route is to the right of the houses at the bottom of the hill, where a path goes downhill past the tiniest of barns. After 150m take another path that forks to the left, which takes you steeply downhill, through a little gate and into a delightful scene. East Gill Beck joins the River Swale here, as it runs over a rocky bed. East Gill Force is a picturesque little waterfall.

Take the wooden footbridge across the Swale, and follow the path that goes left, at first, and then bears right to arrive at the top of the waterfall. At this point – as a finger-post sign indicates – you are walking a short section shared by two long-distance walks: the Pennine Way and Alfred Wainwright's Coast to Coast Walk.

Follow a broad track to the right, through a gate. Keep to this stony track, which follows – but at a much higher level – the course of the River Swale. The river rushes through a deep ravine at this point; if the trees are bare of leaves you may get a glimpse of the double waterfalls that comprise Kisdon Force. To take a good view of them, however, you need to approach them from the opposite side of the river: a fine stroll, but one for another day.

Keld and Swinner Gill Walk

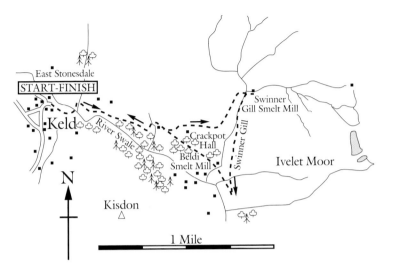

On reaching a gate across the track, you can scramble just a few yards up the hill to the left to discover the entrance (almost blocked up) of a mine: New Level. Continue along the track. After about half a mile the path goes sharp left and then right, the better to cross a little beck. The view to the right now begins to dominate: a splendid panorama looking over the steep-sided valley. The River Swale flows like a silvery ribbon between Black Hill to the left and Kisdon Hill to the right. The slope of the hills makes this view change subtly as you walk. On a clear day it is spectacular; on a wet day it will make you feel less miserable about getting drenched.

If you look left you will see the spoil heaps from the Beldi Hill Mines. A few yards further and you will come across the 'skeleton' of an unroadworthy tractor. Take the stony track that goes left, uphill, almost immediately after it. You will soon arrive at the ruins of lonely Crackpot Hall: occupied as late as the 1950s but lost to dereliction. Can any house in the Dales have enjoyed a finer view than Crackpot Hall? The unstable remains have been demolished, though you can still see a paved yard at the back, and a sheep dipping trough.

Lead Mining in the Yorkshire Dales

Behind the ruins, uphill and to the left, is the entrance to a mining level. Further uphill is a seven-bay bouseteam in poor repair. Beyond the extensive spoil heaps is another level entrance. Head towards a solitary building a little further uphill. This was the blacksmith's shop; inside you can still see the hearth. Walk past the smithy on a well-defined path.

To the right, the valley of Swaledale opens up; Muker is the village in the middle distance. The path levels off as you approach a gate; from here you will get a good view up Swinner Gill and, in the distance, the diminutive smelt mill which is your next objective. Through the gate continue along an increasingly stony path beneath crags that rear up on the left. The path becomes grassy and easier to walk as it makes a gradual descent into the steep-sided valley of Swinner Gill.

As you walk you will be able to see more clearly the position of the smelt mill: above a small waterfall. Next to the waterfall is an entrance to a mining level. Walk downhill and cross Hind Hole Beck on a little stone bridge to arrive at the mining complex.

The smelt mill occupies one of the few areas of level ground in the vicinity. A footpath follows East Grain Beck steeply to the east; if you followed it you would cross the moors into Gunnerside Gill, a mining area explored on Walk One.

Swinner Gill Mill dates from 1804. Ore for this mill, owned by Lord Pomfret, was brought over the gill bridge from the Swinner Gill mines on the west side of the side-valley. This small mill is much reduced in height, and the accumulated rubble makes it hard to visualise the internal layout.

The building is in the form of two rooms. The one on the left housed a set of bellows and a waterwheel of 6 metre diameter mounted against the far wall; the other room contained two ore hearths. From the back of the building a flue emerges and climbs up the hillside. The flue – short by the standards of most other mills in the Dales – is collapsed. It ends in a square chimney, of which only a few stones remain.

A few yards uphill from the mill building is a vertical mining shaft, now covered for safety with a metal grille. But you can at least look down and admire the stonework lining the shaft which continues as far as can be seen.

Having investigated this remote and austere site, retrace your steps to the stone bridge. Twenty yards past the bridge, take a lesser path to the left, leading down towards the beck. The path descends, quite steeply in places, to the beck. Unless the beck is in spate you should have no trouble picking your way across and locating a track that continues up the east side of Swinner Gill. The path provides easy walking, but in places there is a steep drop to the right, so watch your step in wet conditions.

Soon, at the point where Swinner Gill opens up into the main Swaledale valley, you will spy the ruins of Beldi Hill Smelt Mill on its precarious and rocky site. The grassy path leads you down to a stony track. Go right along the track and cross the beck again – this time on a wooden footbridge – to reach the old mill.

Beldi Hill Mill is rather cramped in style, in comparison with other mills. This is due simply to the constraints of the site, with the mill building being 'shoehorned' into the limited space available between a rocky crag to the west and the beck to the east. The sound of water is ever-present, owing to a waterfall a few yards up the beck.

The Beldi Hill Mill was built by the Parkes brothers in 1770. It is rectangular in shape – divided into two parts by a wheel pit that once contained a waterwheel almost 8 metres in diameter. It powered a set of bellows, which fanned the flames of three reverberatory furnaces. A roasting hearth was housed in a separate, square building. The flue was constructed, with some ingenuity, to climb up the adjacent crag. It is now dilapidated, along with the square chimney at the top.

When your explorations are over, you go through a gate to continue along the wide track uphill. Before long you will reach the remains of the tractor that you saw earlier in the day. You should simply retrace your steps from here; remember to leave the track a few yards past East Gill Force. Cross the Swale on the wooden footbridge to arrive back in Keld.

Walk Three

Old Gang & Surrender

The Old Gang mining field exploits the rich Friarfold veins where they cross Hard Level Gill. To walk this remote valley, lying in remote country between Swaledale and Arkengarthdale, is to find yourself in the very heart of the lead mining fields of the northern Dales. The waters of Old Gang Beck (also variously called Mill Beck and Barney Beck) powered two smelt mills: Surrender and Old Gang. The name 'Old Gang', incidentally, means 'old road'.

Mines and Mills

Surrender Mill was built in 1839, to replace a pair of seventeenth century mills that were, by 1818, reported to have been in poor repair. The mining lease in that year stipulated that the old mills be demolished and a new one built, giving the option of reusing some of the stone. To Surrender Mill, just a few metres from Surrender Bridge, came ore won from a number of mines, including the Sir Francis Mine in Gunnerside Gill. This compact and symmetrical building contained four hearths: three for ore and one for slag. To the north of the furnaces are ore stores, with chutes in their rear walls. Separate flues leave the back of the building, then join together to create the main flue that extends 500m up the hill, ending in a (now ruined) chimney of rectangular section.

A waterwheel of approximately 7m in diameter was sited centrally in the mill, between the hearths, in a room that also housed the bellows. Water was carried in a wooden launder from the beck, leaving the waterwheel pit via a covered channel. There are traces of another waterwheel pit, below the mill and nearer the beck; this wheel may have powered the ore crushers. A few metres from the mill are the remains of a 12-bay peat store, measuring 63m long by 5m wide. The mill had a working life of only about 40 years; the last consignment of ore was smelted at Surrender Mill in 1881.

Little over a mile away from Surrender Mill, on a level site just above the beck, are the more substantial remains of the Old Gang Smelt Mill. Though few of the roofs still stand to their original height, this group of buildings is nevertheless an impressive sight. At one time there were other buildings nearby, including offices, stables, gunpowder store, smithy and joiner's shop.

Old Gang Mill is not all of a piece. The main part of the building dates from about 1828; the older part (late 18th century) is on a raised terrace at the back. The newer building has five hearths: four for ore, one for slag. The small building with the square chimney almost certainly housed a roasting hearth, in which some of the sulphur and antimony was driven off prior to smelting in the ore hearths.

Four arched flues leave at the back of the mill, and pass through the ruins of the older mill building. The flues soon combine to form one flue that extends up Healaugh Crag for more than a kilometre to a ruined chimney, about 170m higher than the mill.

The dressed stone from the ore hearths was removed in 1933, and incorporated into the Methodist Chapel in Muker. A pit at the western end of the mill shows where the waterwheel (8m in diameter) was turned by water brought from two dams to the east of the mill. Instead of the more usual system of bellows, there was an air-blast pump housed in a small chamber next to the wheel.

Uphill from the mill is a curious building, fully 120m long but just 7m wide, and divided into three sections. It was used for storing peat, one of the main fuels to fire the ore furnaces. The building is impressive, even though the thatched roof has long gone. Peat was cut only during the summer months; the building is so large because it had to accommodate a whole year's supply. The sides were open to allow a through-put of air to dry the peat.

Lead Mining in the Yorkshire Dales

Coal – another much-used fuel, especially in the latter years of smelting – was brought from the Tan Hill collieries along an old road that stretches for miles in a north-easterly direction across inhospitable moorland.

The Old Gang mining field was owned by the Pomfret and Denys families, from whom it was leased, in 1811, by George and Thomas Alderson. They made the mistake of employing a mining agent called John Davies, who was already working for the owners. Both dishonest in his financial dealings and inexpert in mining matters, he conspired to swindle both parties. When the extent of his incompetence was discovered, Davies was dismissed, and another agent was taken on. Truly, the choice of agent could make or break a mine's prospects.

The Old Gang Mill smelted ore from a number of mining fields. The arched entrances to Hard and Spence levels can be found a few yards west of the mill. Hard Level was known as Force Level when it was started by Lord Pomfret in 1785 to exploit the Old Rake and Friarfold veins. The change of name to the Hard Level was probably in recognition of how tough an enterprise it turned out to be.

Hard Level was eventually linked to many other levels; when the mines were worked it was possible for a miner to enter Hard Level and emerge into daylight via Bunton Level in Gunnerside Gill. By taking another subterranean route he could also negotiate the Moulds Level to reach ground level in Arkengarthdale: it is a remarkable mining complex.

Rails once emerged from these levels, allowing tubs of bouse to be pushed straight onto the dressing floor. This dressing floor, which was in use by 1805, lies between these levels and the mill. The smelt mill was virtually redundant by 1890, though – as in many other lead mining sites – spoil heaps were still being reworked well into our own century.

The Walk

Park: Surrender Bridge, where the minor road between Low Row and Langthwaite crosses Old Gang Beck (SD 989 999). Map: OS Outdoor Leisure 30 (Yorkshire Dales, Northern & Central). Length: 6 miles (10km). Grading: Moderate.

Take a stony track (signed as a bridleway, with no access to vehicles), immediately to the north of Surrender Bridge, to follow Old Gang Beck upstream. The environs of this little river are very rocky: the legacy of centuries of lead mining. Your immediate destination soon comes into view ahead: the Old Gang Smelt Mill, wedged into the valley bottom by extensive spoil heaps. The square chimney, still standing to its full height, is the most visible landmark. The group of buildings forms an evocative ruin.

Just beyond the mill, and up to the right, is the peat store – now reduced to a double row of stone pillars. To the left is the dressing floor. Beneath the left-hand end of the peat store (and at the base of a small hush) can be found the entrance to Spence Level. Beyond a couple of small buildings, you pass a bridge over the beck: an arch made from a single layer of dressed stone, now turfed over.

Continue along the track, uphill, with the beck to your left. Pass (but don't cross) another bridge over the beck. Another track joins from the right, as you walk downhill again, and pass the remains of a dressing floor. At a gate you come to the more substantial Level House Bridge; a track crosses it towards Old Rake Hush and the Old Gang Mines. Pass a ruined building – Level House – with hushes extending to left and right. The track gets rougher, and the valley narrower and rockier, before you emerge onto open moorland – probably with just grouse for company.

Cross and recross the beck, which at this point is merely a stream, to arrive, amid spoil heaps, at a wooden gate. If you thought the valley was bleak and cheerless, it now gets worse, as the rocky track now bears right, uphill, into a 'moonscape' of mining debris. This is the Friarfold mining field: one of the most productive in Swaledale,

Lead Mining in the Yorkshire Dales

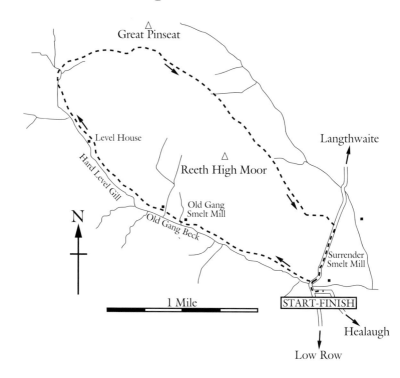

which extends west into Gunnerside Gill and east, towards Langthwaite, into the Hungry Hushes.

Though the path becomes indistinct, you only have to follow the broad swathe of rocky mined waste uphill, with a few little cairns to guide you. At the top of the hill – Great Pinseat – keep to the right of a larger cairn with a post sticking out of it, as the track levels out. It's worth stopping, before the descent, to scan the horizons of both Swaledale and Arkengarthdale, for more evidence of mining as far as the eye can see.

Soon you leave the mining debris behind, to walk downhill on a rutted, grassy track towards the rounded contours of Calver Hill. Pass a large sheepfold on the left, then the 'skeleton' of a van, for which

Old Gang and Surrender Walk

the MOT test is now but a distant memory. Your path is unmistakable, through heather and coarse, tussocky grass, passing bell pits on your left and a line of grouse butts on your right. When you meet the minor road that links the hamlets of Langthwaite and Low Row, walk right, downhill, to arrive back at Surrender Bridge.

This is your opportunity to take a look around the ruins of Surrender Mill and the peat store nearby.

Walk Four

Grassington Moor

Grassington is one of the National Park's 'honeypot' villages, where visitors congregate in large numbers on summer weekends and Bank Holidays. Here, too, can be found the National Park's administrative offices, next to the Tourist Information Centre. Visitors could be forgiven for overlooking the village's lead mining connections, as Grassington is more concerned with catering for tourists than in explaining its mining history. Some information – and a number of relics – can be found, however, in the excellent little folk museum in the village's cobbled square. To see the mining field you should drive (or walk) up past the square to the top of the village, and take Moor Road, which peters out – as a metalled road, at least – at Yarnbury, at one time the mining offices of the extensive mining field of Grassington Moor which stretches out before you.

Mines and Mills

Grassington Moor is a different kind of mining area to those found in Swaledale and Arkengarthdale. Here are no steep-sided valleys – and therefore few of the rocky hushes – that typify the mining fields of, say, Gunnerside Gill or Grinton. The flatter expanses of Grassington Moor were riddled, instead, with a tracery of bell-pits and shafts. These mines primarily exploited the productive Bycliff Vein, which extended for eight miles between Conistone Moor in Wharfedale, almost to Pateley Bridge in Nidderdale.

Grassington Moor has a long history of being mined – in piecemeal fashion – by small groups of adventurers. The first mining records date back to the 15th century, when the monks of Fountains

Abbey worked a smelt mill. But from the end of the 18th century the fortunes of the mining field became inextricably linked with those of the Duke of Devonshire. Along with ownership of the mineral rights, he was able to collect the royalties.

During the productive decade from 1750 to 1760, at least 150 men were working at the Grassington Moor mines. At this time the output was 600 tons per year; twenty years later this amount had halved. By 1790 the Grassington Moor mines were becoming exhausted, and it was increasingly difficult to get ore out by horse whim. As the miners drove deeper, the shafts became prone to flooding. Grassington Moor had already been mined continuously for two centuries. There were no new veins to find, only better ways to exploit those already discovered. The Duke of Devonshire, whose country seat was in Derbyshire, was able to do what no small team of mining adventurers could do: take a longer-term view of the mining operations and sink venture capital into a planned mining strategy. His foresight seems to have paid off handsomely, and it was said that the building of Chatsworth House, his family seat, was largely paid for by the profits from lead mining.

In 1790 the Duke appointed as his mineral agent one Cornelius Flint, who divided his time between the Duke's mines in Grassington and those in Derbyshire. He set about draining waterlogged mines on Grassington Moor – the main thrust of the project being the driving of the Duke's Level from lower down in Hebden Gill. Flint intended the Duke's Level to be a boat level, to make it easier to get ore out of the mines. However, the level was built to narrower dimensions, and with the single purpose of unwatering the mines further up on Grassington Moor, by means of a complex arrangement of cross-cuts. This drainage level eventually linked many of the levels in the extensive mining field, and helped to breathe new life into what, by the latter years of the 18th century, had looked like a worked-out field. Productivity increased tenfold in the decade from 1820, as the Duke's Level made possible the driving of deeper shafts.

On the surface, too, new connections were being forged. The Cupola Mill was built in 1792, superceding Low Mill (which was by the River Wharfe, close to Linton Church). The new mill was equipped with a pair of reverberatory furnaces. This kind of furnace needed to be run continuously, with a good throughput of ore, so the conditions of many mining leases stipulated that all mined ore had to be smelted at Cupola Mill.

Another reverberatory furnace was added in 1830, plus a roasting furnace and a slag-hearth, with the furnaces powered by a 7m diameter waterwheel. The original 60m flue was extended (incorporating a pair of condensers), rising 150m up the slope to a chimney. A complex arrangement of flues, 2km in total length, meant that whole sections could be isolated (for cleaning or repair) without the need to take the expensive step of shutting down the mill.

The Duke's New Road was built in the 1830s for ease of transport between the mine offices at Yarnbury and the Cupola Mill. It offered a more direct route – and gentler gradients – than the original road, Old Moor Lane, the continuation of the road from Grassington to Yarnbury. A light railway line was also built for carrying ore from Barratt's Incline at Yarnbury, through the dressing and smelting processes.

Many of those who put up money for turnpike roads in the 1750s were already investors in the mines on Grassington Moor, so it was in their own interest to develop a good road system. The turnpike road between Grassington and Pateley Bridge took a direct route over the high ground at Greenhow Hill, thus serving the mining fields in both Wharfedale and Nidderdale. The Leeds and Liverpool Canal, open by 1774, offered a better way of transporting lead to the ports, and bringing in supplies of coal, the principal fuel for the smelt mill. Indeed, the canal wharf at Gargrave was primarily built to serve the mines of Grassington Moor.

Considering the problems created by flooded mine-workings, it is ironic that water had to be diverted to all parts of the mining field. With no fast-flowing streams to turn the waterwheels, the mining engineers used great ingenuity to ensure a consistent head of water for powering the crushers, pumps, winding gear, aerial ropeways, and other mining processes.

Grassington Moor Walk

Priest's Tarn, some distance from the main mining area, and at the highest point of Grassington Moor, was dammed to form a substantial reservoir. A water-course was built to convey water from the tarn and maintain the levels in a succession of smaller reservoirs.

The Duke's High and Low water-courses furthered this idea. A series of dams were built across Blea Beck, to conserve water when the beck was full. In dry weather the water from these reservoirs (nine in all) could be diverted into the water-courses. The water-courses extended for a total of six-and-a-half convoluted miles over Grassington Moor, all draining, eventually, into Coalgrove Beck. They represented an imaginative solution to a perennial problem, and powered eight full-size waterwheels.

The output of the Grassington Moor mines peaked in the 1850s and 1860s, with 2,000 tons during 1865. This represented Grassington Moor's highest yield, indicating both good prices and a buoyant market. Within ten years this figure had declined, tragically, to barely 200 tons. By 1877 underground mining had ceased; after that date there was just a little reworking of spoil heaps. The last load of lead was smelted at Cupola Mill in 1882. For the remaining years of the 19th century, the dwindling requirements for lead were met by the mines in Swaledale and Arkengarthdale.

The Walk

Start: Yarnbury (SE 015 659). Map: OS Outdoor Leisure 10 (Yorkshire Dales, Southern). Distance: 3 miles (5km). Easy.

Drive through Grassington village and take Moor Road ahead. After about 2 miles the metalled road peters out to a stony track at Yarnbury, a cluster of sturdy houses sheltered by trees. Park here. When the Grassington Moor mines were being worked, Yarnbury House was where the mine agent lived. Other buildings, behind Yarnbury House, had mining uses: smithy, store, carpenter's shop, etc. A couple of these buildings are now dwellings. The small building close to the track was the weigh-house, where miners' ore

Lead Mining in the Yorkshire Dales

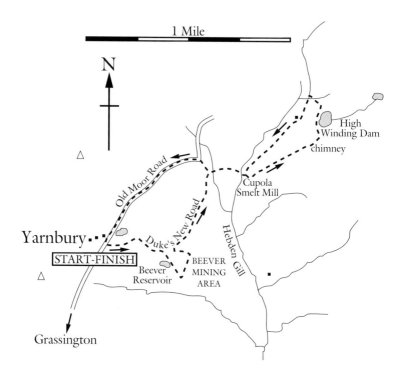

was weighed before it was transported away from Grassington Moor.

Take a substantial track to the right, opposite the houses, signed as a footpath to Hebden. This is the Duke's New Road, constructed during the 1830s to provide a more direct link between Yarnbury and the Cupola smelt mill.

Immediately across a cattle grid you find substantial mining remains. To your left is Yarnbury Dam, fed by the Duke's Watercourse, which provided water to power a wheel on the dressing floor nearby. A railway, dating back to the 1820s, carried ore from Barratt's Incline to the dressing floor; a few of the stone sleepers can still be seen. To the right of the track are spoil heaps and an area of bell-pits.

Continue along the track, soon leaving it to walk right, and skirt the little reservoir known as Beever Dam. Cross a wall-stile to arrive in another area of mining waste. Here you will find Beever's Engine Shaft: about 120m deep and now capped for safety. Beneath the shaft are scant remains of bouseteams. Nearby is the Beever wheel-house, though more modern reworkings of spoil-heaps for their barytes content have destroyed most of the original building. A little further down the track that leads into Hebden Gill is an isolated powder house.

A sandy track bearing left from the Beever workings allows you to rejoin the Duke's New Road. Bear right along it, towards the chimney you see on the horizon. Follow the track, to cross rocky Hebden Gill on a high embankment; a grassy track soon forks to the right and takes you to the Cupola smelt mill. Follow the main flue behind the mill (walk beside it, not on top of it) towards the chimney on the hilltop.

You soon come to a pair of stone-lined pits: all that now remains of condensers which helped to collect vapourised lead that would otherwise have been lost. The elaborate system of flues were constructed when the Cupola Mill needed to work continuously. Sections of flue could be isolated for the purposes of repair or recovery of lead, without the need to let the funaces cool down. You can see some of these junctions in the flue system, and admire both the masonry skills and the ingenuity of the design. All the flues unite at the top of the hill, at the handsome chimney. As a plaque attests, it was restored in 1971 by the Earby Mines Research Group.

Continue uphill, past the chimney, to reach High Winding Dam: another of the reservoirs created to power the many waterwheels of the mining fields. Beyond the dam is the pit that once housed one of these wheels.

Make your way left, towards a more modern collection of buildings and workings. These belonged to Dales Chemicals, a company which operated from 1956 to 1964 to rework old spoil-heaps. Join the stony track which winds downhill through a scene of mining devastation that extends over a wide area. Continue downhill, passing the Cupola Mill once again. Immediately beyond the embankment taking the track over Hebden Gill, bear right on a grassy path to a gate. Bear left, uphill; this is Old Moor Lane, and it takes you, after a few minutes walking, back to Yarnbury.

Just 100m before Yarnbury House, look out for Barratt's Incline, which, as indicated by a datestone on the arched entrance, was driven in 1829, by Capt Barratt, then the Duke of Devonshire's Cornish mining engineer. The incline provided a link to all the major shafts in the mining field, and provided an alternative route for bringing lead out of the mines and delivering it to the nearby dressing floor.

Walk Five

Langthwaite

The most northerly dale in the National Park, Arkengarthdale is a side valley that branches away from Swaledale at the village of Reeth, where the waters of Arkle Beck join the River Swale. The village's position at the junction of these two dales, and their extensive mining fields, made Reeth effectively the lead mining capital of the northern Dales.

If you take the road signposted to Arkengarthdale and Tan Hill (it branches off next to the Buck Inn in Reeth), you will pass Langthwaite, where this walk starts and finishes. Continue along the road and you will soon find that farmsteads, barns and even dry stone walls disappear, as the view opens up to the north. Stainmoor – mile after mile of uninterrupted wasteland – looms ahead. You keep driving, becoming ever more convinced that this road can't possibly be going anywhere you'd want to go.

But there you'd be wrong for, just as that thought is developing into a cast-iron certainty, you crest a little hill and ahead of you – like some mirage – is the welcoming sight of the Tan Hill Inn. This windswept pub, famously double-glazed and still reliant on a generator for its electricity, has earned its place in the *Guinness Book of Records* as the highest pub in England.

Mines and Mills

Reeth, arranged around its extensive, sloping green, was once a town of some importance. At the height of the lead mining industry, in the middle of the 19th century, Reeth's population topped 1,500. Now it is but a third of that number. The Reeth of today is thronged with tourists' cars in summer, and there are few reminders – apart from some interesting exhibits in the Swaledale Folk Museum – that it was lead mining that brought prosperity to Reeth.

By taking the Arkengarthdale road you will soon be climbing along the shoulder of Calver Hill, with views of steep-sided Fremington Edge opening to your right, beyond Arkle Beck. The first collection of houses is Arkle Town: a town in name only. Next comes Langthwaite, the largest settlement in the dale and well-known to fans of the James Herriot television dramas for its appearance on the opening credits. In 1851 Langthwaite was a substantial village of 74 houses, where fairs and hiring markets were regularly held. Now it's a peaceful backwater. To get an impression of how the population has declined over the last hundred years, just take a look at the size of the village's Anglican church and Methodist chapel.

At the height of the lead mining industry, Arkengarthdale had no fewer than nine public houses including, confusingly, two CB Inns. Today there are but two inns (apart from remote Tan Hill): the Red Lion in Langthwaite and, a mile further up the road, the one surviving CB Inn. It, too, merits a place in the *Guinness Book of Records*, with a claim to having the shortest name of any pub in the country. A few years ago the name was expanded to The Charles Bathurst Inn; today it is the CB once again. The lead mining connection may not be immediately obvious, but more of the Bathurst family in due course.

Continue along the road; soon a road forks to the right (signposted to Barnard Castle). Just beyond this junction, in the middle of a field, is an architectural gem: a diminutive, hexagonal building known as the powder house, built about 1800. Here were stored the candles and gunpowder used in the lead mines, and it was sited well away from other buildings for obvious reasons.

Langthwaite boasted two major lead smelting mills, one on either side of the road you are travelling. It would be nice to report that they are in as good condition as the little powder house, but this is not, alas, the case.

The Octagon Mill, dating from 1804, was the largest smelt mill built in the Yorkshire Dales and a splendid example of industrial architecture. The mill was 33m long and 21m wide, with huge trusses to support the expansive roof; it was, as its name suggests, eight-sided. Inside were four furnaces and a massive waterwheel; during the last century it was the prime smelting site for ore from the CB mines. Once the furnaces had gone cold for the last time, the mill saw further service as a sawmill. But after the roof was removed, during the 1940s, the building deteriorated rapidly. This handsome building was reduced to rubble, and now stands no higher than its foundations, to the right of the road you are travelling.

Langthwaite New Mill, on the opposite side of the road, is in a similarly ruinous condition, though the path of its long double flue can still be traced up the hillside, where it joins the remains of the flue from the Octagon Mill, and ends with the ruins of what had been a sizeable chimney. This mill (also known as the CB Mill) was built to replace an earlier building – the Moulds Mill – which stood on a hillside to the west of Langthwaite village. To the west of Langthwaite is a remarkable scene of mining devastation, known as the Hungry Hushes. Deep, rocky, wholly man-made valleys – where barely a blade of grass now grows – extend for hundreds of metres.

The road continues past a little village that glories in the name of Whaw; from here the landscape becomes increasingly bleak as you approach Tan Hill Inn. Poor quality coal was mined nearby, at the Tan Hill Colliery. Coal from here was transported across the fells to fire a number of the smelt mills in the northern Dales.

The main player in the story of Arkengarthdale's lead mining was the CB Company. Records show that the manor of Arkengarthdale was bought, in 1656, by Dr John Bathurst, who had ministered to the health of Oliver Cromwell. Both his son and his grandson were called Charles, and it was the latter who lent his initials to both the mining company and a brace of pubs. He developed a number of mines in the dale; he and his descendants were to have a great effect in the area during the next 270 years. In fact, the Arkengarthdale mines survived longer than many of those in Swaledale. The remote Faggergill mines, for example, were still being worked in 1912.

Lead Mining in the Yorkshire Dales

The Walk

Start: Langthwaite (NZ 005 024). Map: OS Outdoor Leisure 30 (Yorkshire Dales, Northern & Central). Length: 3 miles (5km). Easy.

Park in the pay and display car park immediately to the south of Langthwaite village. Walk right, along the road, and take the first road to the right, across the bridge over Arkle Beck, and into the tiny village of Langthwaite. Opposite the Red Lion Inn, take a track to the right, between sturdy stone houses, that soon runs by the side of Arkle Beck. Pass a sewage treatment works, footbridge and barn, as the track bears left, away from the beck, to follow the edge of a wood. At a fork of tracks, keep left, uphill (signed Bridleway), soon getting good views ahead of Fremington Edge.

Walk through two metal gates, to another fork of tracks. The right fork goes down to Storthwaite Farm; your route, however, is straight ahead – signed to Slei Gill. Enjoy level walking on a grassy path, following Slei Gill Beck to your right. Through a hole in a wall you come to the first evidence of mining: spoil heaps, mining debris and hushes to left and right. The hush on the far side of the beck is particularly impressive, and extends to the top of Fremington Edge.

Cross a stile and continue along the grassy track, above the rubble-strewn beck. You soon come to an area of large, bare, spoil heaps. The path winds between two of these spoil heaps. On the left is the rocky gorge of Old Rake Hush. The valley broadens out, and the beck is almost choked with rocks: what has been left after many years of hushing. On the far side of the beck is the arched entrance to a mining level, Sun Gutter Level, out of which water runs. There are hushes on both sides of Slei Gill: it's a fascinating – though desolate – sight.

Cross a tumble-down wall and continue uphill on a rockier path. Pass a series of little waterfalls as the valley narrows and becomes steeper-sided. Follow a wall to a gate and to Washy Green Mine, as far up Slei Gill as this walk extends. The prominent stone structure is a waterwheel pit, with an aperture at the front to allow the water to rejoin the beck. This would make a good sandwich stop.

Langthwaite Walk

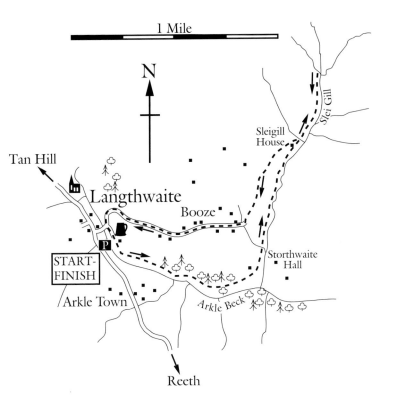

Retrace your steps from here to the tumble-down wall. Immediately beyond the wall, bear right, uphill, on another grassy track. Enjoy elevated views down into Slei Gill, with the rounded contours of Calver Hill filling the distant view ahead. You soon come to Sleigill House, now almost ruinous, but a home for lead miners until the end of the last century.

Continue along the track, and cross a series of hushes. Look out on the left for a mining level – Proctor's Level – driven into the base of Tanner Rake Hush. This hush, worked for at least two centuries, is one of the longest in the Dales.

Lead Mining in the Yorkshire Dales

Soon you come to the highest part of the walk, affording good views back to Sleigill House and the steep-sided valley beyond, and the hushes and spoil heaps, before the track goes through a gate. Follow deep tractor ruts around a barn and into the straggle of houses – some ruined, some still in good heart – that comprise the tiny hamlet of Booze. Saddled with a name that conjures up all kinds of images in the mind's eye, Booze probably just means 'the house by the bend'; another possible derivation is from the miners' word, 'bouse'. When the Slei Gill mines were in full production, during the middle years of the last century, more than two hundred people lived in Booze. If Langthwaite is peaceful today, then Booze is positively soporific – being connected to the mains electricity supply as recently as the 1960s. Follow the track, which offers good views down to Arkle Town. The track becomes metalled and leads down, steeply at the end, into Langthwaite's compact cluster of houses.

Walk Six

Grinton

This short walk visits what is probably the best-preserved – and the most visited – lead-smelting mill in the Yorkshire Dales. Many mills have disappeared, falling into dereliction, or dismantled to recycle the dressed stone for new buildings. Others were considered safety hazards, or presented all too visible targets for vandalism. So we can be grateful that Grinton Mill has given yeoman service, in the century since the furnaces last roared, in a variety of agricultural uses.

This secondary usage has ensured that the fabric of the building has been kept in good repair. This is the only smelt mill in the Dales still to be fully roofed. Realising the building's importance, the National Park had all the slates removed in 1987, numbering each one, and repaired the stone and woodwork. The slates were then replaced in their original positions. The walls have been pointed and consolidated, to avoid further deterioration. The roof represents quite an architectural achievement, with roof-beams and trusses on a massive scale. The main beams – of hand-sawn pine – span the entire width of the building, without the need of any further support. The roof timbers are joined together with wooden pegs.

The interior of the mill has, however, seen many changes. The National Park has, as yet, resisted the temptation to create a full-blown 'heritage site', in the manner of Killhope in Weardale, though this is one of the few lead mining sites in the Dales that could be restored to something like its former glory. The mill is much visited because it is situated conveniently close to the minor road linking Grinton and Leyburn.

The mill was built in Cogden Gill, about a mile south of Grinton village. This site, at the meeting of Cogden Beck and Smales Beck, provided a level site, a good supply of water and close proximity to the mining fields on the southern flank of Swaledale. The original course of the beck would have been beneath where the mill now stands. The water-course was diverted, culverted and partly covered over to create more usable space around the mill.

The buildings we see today date from about 1820 (and were built on the foundations of an earlier mill), though lead from the adjacent How Vein had been mined and processed here for at least six centuries before this date. From 1733, until the lease lapsed, the mill was operated by the London Lead Company, whose Quaker ideals helped to create a more humane working environment than was common in most Pennine mines.

The company exploited the Grinton mines very successfully. The lead smelted at Grinton Mill came from a number of mining fields south of the River Swale, including Harkerside, Grinton Moor, Whitaside and Summer Lodge. These mines were the subject of acrimonious disputes for many years. In order to accommodate the larger amounts of ore to be smelted, the mill's ore hearths were taken out and replaced by a pair of reverberatory furnaces. Grinton Mill was last used for smelting lead in 1886.

Here at Grinton Mill you can get a good idea of the smelting process. Even the most casual observer will be able to imagine the mill as it was when the waterwheel was operating massive bellows which, in turn, kept the furnaces at the high temperatures needed for smelting. The main building is 18m by by 12m, with walls almost one metre thick in places. The two reverberatory furnaces are obvious features, as are the vents, or tuyères, at the back through which air was blown to bring the furnaces up to smelting temperature. This job was done by bellows, though early last century they were replaced by an air-pump: more efficient than bellows though still powered by a waterwheel.

Both the wheel and the air-pump are gone, but the original wooden frame that supported the air-pump is still in place. The waterwheel pit was filled in, once the mill was given over to agricultural uses, to provide a level floor. The size of the wheel (7m in diameter) can be gauged, however, by the height of the water leat, or launder, still *in situ* just beneath the roof beams. A door between the two parts of the mill was built after smelting had ended, as was a trench to either side of the door, which was used as a sheep-dip.

Water was brought into the mill along a wooden leat from further up the gill. Cogden Beck runs freely in winter; in summer it is a mere trickle. It is supplemented, however, immediately to the south of the mill, by a spring that never dries up. A dam was built a few metres upstream from the mill to create a small reservoir, which ensured a good head of water throughout the year.

The flue from the mill can be traced from the ore hearths, along the southern wall of the peat store, and straight up Sharrow Hill. Lined with stone and grassed over, the flue extends about 400m uphill to the site of a chimney. Parts of the flue have collapsed, but enough of it remains to show the quality of the stonemasons' workmanship. Slightly uphill from the mill is the peat store, still in fair condition thanks to having doubled as a cow-house for many years. Here would have been stored enough fuel to last a full year.

The Walk

Start: Grinton (SE 047 984). Map: OS Outdoor Leisure 30 (Yorkshire Dales, Northern & Central). Length: 4 miles (7km). Easy.

This walk has Grinton smelt mill as its destination. The mill is much visited, not least because it lies conveniently near a road. If you merely want to investigate the mill, park on the Grinton-Leyburn road (map ref: SE 049 969). Park in Grinton (alternatively, there are convenient parking places at the junction of the Leyburn and Redmire roads, map ref: SE 047 977).

From the Bridge Inn and Grinton church, take the road uphill, signed to Leyburn and Redmire. When the road forks after a cattle grid, keep straight on (signed to Leyburn) to pass a rather incongruous, castellated building, which enjoys panoramic views over Swaledale. Once a shooting lodge, it is now a Youth Hostel,

Lead Mining in the Yorkshire Dales

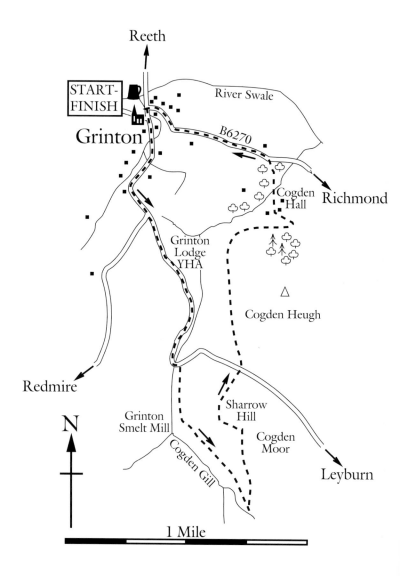

Reeth

START-FINISH

Grinton

River Swale

B6270

Cogden Hall

Richmond

Grinton Lodge YHA

Redmire

Grinton Smelt Mill

Cogden Heugh

Cogden Gill

Sharrow Hill

Cogden Moor

Leyburn

N

1 Mile

sheltered from the wind by a belt of trees. Continue up the unenclosed road, onto open moorland. After about a mile of road-walking, you cross Cogden Beck at a sharp hairpin bend. When the road briefly dips, after the bend, bear right along a substantial track, signed as a bridleway. Follow the track to arrive shortly at Grinton Mill, sited snugly in this little side valley, with its peat store nearby.

There is a choice of paths up Cogden Gill. Continue on the track which passes the top of the peat store, or take a path on the opposite side of Cogden Beck. Both paths meet up again further up the valley. About 70m upstream from the mill, look out for a grassy dam, which was used to maintain a small reservoir.

The path rejoins the track about 500m from the mill, in an area of old spoil heaps. Bear right, uphill, along the track, onto the heather moorland. Crest the first brow of the hill, as the track becomes grassy. About 200m before a stone cairn is a second dam, heather-covered and rather indistinct, which was created to conserve water for the mill's waterwheel. Bear acute left here. There is only a barely discernible path through the heather. No problem: just aim for the hill at the top of the mill's flue.

This high-level section offers good views to the left, towards some of the hushes and mines where the lead for Grinton smelt mill was won. The path is easier to follow as you approach the top of the mill's flue. A pile of stones is all that remains of the chimney that once stood here, on the top of Sharrow Hill. Walk 30m down the flue, then bear right just before an undamaged section of flue. Join a grassy track to pass beneath an old quarry.

Below the track here is an old limekiln. There are limekilns to be found throughout the Dales, generally close to limestone outcrops, where farmers would burn limestone to sweeten the sour moorland soil. But this example is of a larger, three-bay design, for the burning of lime on an industrial scale. Enjoy long views towards Reeth, Calver Hill and Arkengarthdale beyond, as you walk down to cross the Grinton-Leyburn road. Through a gate, take a rutted track downhill through a pleasant pasture of heather and bracken. Continue through two more gates, enjoying views of Swaledale and Cogden

Beck. The track makes a wide loop before descending to Cogden Hall. Walk between farm buildings to take the farm track down to the B6270 Reeth-Richmond road. Bear left along the road; within ten minutes you will be back in the village of Grinton.

Places to Visit

The following museums have exhibits that relate to lead mining:

Museum of Yorkshire Dales Lead Mining, Old Grammer School, School Lane, Earby, Colne, Lancashire. Tel: 01282-841422.

Craven Museum, Town Hall, High Street, Skipton, North Yorkshire BD23 1AH. Tel: 01756-794079.

Richmondshire Museum, Ryders Wynd, Richmond, North Yorkshire DL10 5DA. Tel: 01748-825611.

Swaledale Folk Museum, Reeth, near Richmond, North Yorkshire. Tel: 01748-884373.

Nidderdale Museum, Council Offices, King Street, Pateley Bridge, North Yorkshire. Tel: 01423-711225.

Dales Countryside Museum, Station Yard, Hawes, Wensleydale, North Yorkshire DL8 3NT. Tel: 01969-667494.

Upper Wharfedale Folk Museum, The Square, Grassington, North Yorkshire. (Peter Sethney 01756 753059).

Phone museums for opening times, or the Yorkshire Dales

Lead Mining in the Yorkshire Dales

National Park: 01756-752748.

Outside the area covered by this book, but well worth a visit:

Cononley Lead Mine. From Bradford-Keighley road (A650), take sign for Cononley; at the top of the village, go left, signed Lothersdale. Bear left at T-junction; drive for a mile to arrive at Cononley Lead Mine, on the left. Leave cars by roadside, and walk to the mine.

Killhope Lead Mining Museum, Cowshill, Bishop Auckland, Co Durham. Tel: 01388-537505.

Nenthead Mines Heritage Centre, Nenthead, Alston, Cumbria CA9 3PD. Tel: 01434-382037.

Peak District Mining Museum, The Pavilion, Matlock Bath, Derbyshire DE4 3PS. Tel: 01629-583834.

Societies

Northern Mine Research Society, The Secretary, c/o 38 Main Street, Sutton in Craven, Keighley, West Yorkshire BD20 7HD.

National Association of Mining History Organisations, The Secretary, c/o Peak District Mining Museum, The Pavilion, Matlock Bath, Derbyshire DE4 3PS.

Historical Metallurgy Society, The Secretary, Department of Economic History, The University, Sheffield S10 2TN.

Index

Index

Other Dalesman titles for walkers

Walks Around Series: Peak District

BAKEWELL Martin Smith £1.99
BUXTON Andrew McCloy £1.99
CASTLETON John Gillham £1.99
MATLOCK Martin Smith £1.99

Walks Around Series: Lake District

AMBLESIDE Tom Bowker £1.99
HAWKSHEAD Mary Welsh £1.99
KESWICK Dawn Gibson £1.99
WINDERMERE Robert Gambles £1.99

Pub Walks Series

LAKE DISTRICT Terry Marsh £5.99
NORTH YORK MOORS & COAST Richard Musgrave £5.99
PEAK DISTRICT John Morrison £5.99
YORKSHIRE DALES Richard Musgrave £5.95

Walking and Trail Guides

LAKE DISTRICT, WESTERN FELLS Paddy Dillon £5.99
LAKE DISTRICT, EASTERN FELLS Paddy Dillon £5.99
WHITE PEAK Martin Smith £4.99
DARK PEAK John Gillham £4.99
NORTH PENNINES Alan Hall £4.99
SOUTH PENNINES John Gillham £4.99
CLEVELAND WAY Martin Collins £4.99
PENNINE WAY Terry Marsh £4.99

Safety for Walkers

MOUNTAIN SAFETY Kevin Walker £4.99
MAP READING Robert Matkin £3.50

Magazines

DALESMAN, CUMBRIA and PEAK AND PENNINE all feature walking
in each monthly issue

Available from all good bookshops.
In case of difficulty contact Dalesman Publishing Company, Clapham Via
Lancaster LA2 8EB. Tel: 015242 51225